TEXAS INSTRUMENTS

TI-81

G U I D E B O O K

Manual developed by: The staff of Texas Instruments Instructional Communications

With contributions by:
Brad Christensen
Franklin Demana
Linda Ferrio
Pat Milheron
John Powers
Tom Prickett
Dave Santucci
Bert K. Waits

Ideas for some of the applications and examples in this manual were taken from *Precalculus Mathematics: A Graphing Approach* by Franklin Demana and Bert K. Waits, published by Addison-Wesley Publishing Company and used by permission of the authors.

FCC Information Concerning Radio Frequency Interference

This equipment has been tested and found to comply with the limits for a Class B digital device, pursuant to Part 15 of the FCC rules. These limits are designed to provide reasonable protection against harmful interference in a residential installation. This equipment generates, uses, and can radiate radio frequency energy and, if not installed and used in accordance with the instructions, may cause harmful interference with radio communications. However, there is no guarantee that interference will not occur in a particular installation.

If this equipment does cause harmful interference to radio or television reception, which can be determined by turning the equipment off and on, you can try to correct the interference by one or more of the following measures:

- Reorient or relocate the receiving antenna.
- Increase the separation between the equipment and receiver.
- Connect the equipment into an outlet on a circuit different from that to which the receiver is connected.
- Consult the dealer or an experienced radio/television technician for help.

Caution: Any changes or modifications to this equipment not expressly approved by Texas Instruments may void your authority to operate the equipment.

This digital apparatus does not exceed the Class B limits for radio noise emissions from digital apparatus set out in the Radio Interference Regulations of the Canadian Department of Communications.

Table of Contents

This manual describes how to use the TI-81 Graphics Calculator. The first chapter gives general instructions on operating the TI-81. Chapters 2 through 8 describe its interactive features.

Table of Contents (Continued)

Table of Contents (Continued)

Using this Manual Effectively

The structure of the TI–81 manual and the design of its pages can help you quickly find the information you need. Consistent presentation techniques are used throughout the manual to make it easy to use.

Structure of the Manual

The manual contains sections that teach you how to use the calculator.

- Getting Started is a fast-paced introduction to several important features of the TI–81.

- Chapter 1 describes general operation and lays the foundation for Chapters 2 through 8.

- Chapters 2 through 8 describe specific functional areas of the TI–81—one per chapter, with short examples showing how to use some of the features described in the chapter.

- Chapter 9 contains application examples that incorporate features from different functional areas of the calculator. These examples can help you see how commands, functions, and instructions work together to accomplish meaningful tasks.

Page-Design Conventions

When possible, units of information are presented on a single page or on two facing pages. Several page-design elements help you find information quickly.

- **Page headings**—The descriptive heading at the top of the page or two-page unit identifies the subject of the unit.

- **General text**—Just below the page heading, a short section of bold text provides general information about the subject covered in the unit.

- **Left-column subheadings**—Each subheading identifies a specific topic or task related to the page or unit subject.

- **Specific text**—The text to the right of a subheading presents detailed information about that specific topic or task. The information may be presented as paragraphs, numbered procedures, bulleted lists, or illustrations.

- **Page "footers"**—The bottom of each page shows the chapter name, chapter number, and page number.

Information-mapping Conventions

Several conventions are used to present information concisely and in an easily referenced format.

- **Tables and charts**—Sets of related information are presented in tables or charts for quick reference.

- **Numbered procedures**—A procedure is a sequence of steps that performs a task. In this manual, each step is numbered in the order in which you must perform it. No other text in the manual is numbered; therefore, when you see numbered text, you know you must perform the steps sequentially.

- **"Bulleted" lists**—If several items have equal importance, or if you may choose one of several alternative actions, this manual precedes each item with a "bullet" (•) to highlight it—like this list you are reading now.

Reference Aids

Several techniques have been used to help you look up specific information when you need it. These include:

- A complete table of contents at the front of the manual, listing the page headings in each chapter.

- A chapter table of contents on the first page of each chapter.

- An alphabetical table of commands in Appendix A, showing their correct formats, the key and menu sequences for accessing them, and page references for more information.

- A table of error codes in Appendix B, showing the codes and their meanings, with problem-handling information.

- An alphabetical index at the back of the manual, listing tasks and topics you may need to look up.

Do this first!

Getting Started

The Getting Started section takes you through several examples to introduce you to some of the principal operating and graphing features of the TI-81. You can save time and effort by completing these examples first.

Contents

The Keyboard

The keys of the TI–81 are grouped by color and physical layout to allow easy location of the key you need. The keys are divided into four zones: graphing keys, editing keys, advanced function keys, and scientific calculator keys.

The Zones of the Keyboard

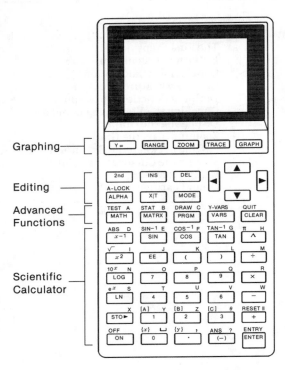

Graphing Keys   These keys are most frequently used to access the interactive graphing features of the TI–81.

Editing Keys   These keys are most frequently used for editing expressions and values.

Advanced Function Keys   These keys are used to access the advanced functions of the TI–81.

Scientific Calculator Keys   These keys are used to access the capabilities of a standard scientific calculator.

The First Steps

Before beginning these sample problems, follow the steps on this page to ensure that the TI-81 is reset to its factory settings. (Resetting the TI-81 erases all previously entered data.)

1. Press ON to turn the calculator on.

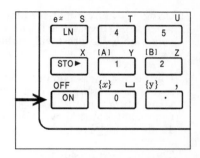

2. Press 2nd and then press +. (Pressing 2nd accesses the function printed to the left above the next key that you press. RESET is the second function of +.)

   The TI-81 displays the RESET menu.

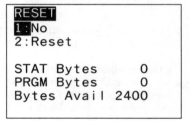

3. Press 2 to select 〈Reset〉, the second item in the RESET menu.

   The display shows the message **Mem cleared**. Press CLEAR to clear the screen.

   If you need to adjust the display contrast, press 2nd and then press ▲ (to make the display darker) or ▼ (to make the display lighter).

Entering a Calculation

The TI-81 display can show up to eight lines of 16 characters per line. This lets you see each expression in its entirety as it is entered. The result is displayed on the following line.

1. Using trial and error, determine when $1000 invested at 6% annual compounded interest will double in value.

   For the first guess, compute the amount available at the end of 10 years. Enter the expression just as you would write it down. Key in 1000 ⨯ 1.06 ^ 10.

   The entire expression is shown in the first line of the display.

```
1000*1.06^10
```

2. Press ENTER to evaluate the expression.

   The result of the expression is shown on the right side of the second line on the display. The cursor is positioned on the left side of the third line, ready for you to enter the next expression.

```
1000*1.06^10
        1790.847697
■
```

3. The next guess should be greater than 10 years. Make the next guess 12 years. To calculate the amount after 12 years, key in 1000 ⨯ 1.06 ^ 12, followed by ENTER.

```
1000*1.06^10
        1790.847697
1000*1.06^12
        2012.196472
```

Continuing a Calculation

To save keystrokes, you can use the Last Entry feature to recall the last expression entered and then edit it for a new calculation. In addition, the next expression can be continued from the previous result.

1. The next guess should be less than, but close to, 12 years. Compute the amount available at the end of 11.9 years, using the Last Entry feature. Press [2nd], followed by [ENTRY] (the second function of [ENTER]).

   The last calculated expression is shown on the next line of the display. The cursor is positioned at the end of this expression.

```
1000*1.06^10
       1790.847697
1000*1.06^12
       2012.196472
1000*1.06^12
```

2. You can edit the expression. Press ◄ to move the cursor over the 2. Then type in 1.9 to change 12 to 11.9. Press [ENTER] to evaluate the expression.

   Note: This process can be continued to obtain a solution with the desired accuracy.

```
1000*1.06^10
       1790.847697
1000*1.06^12
       2012.196472
1000*1.06^11.9
       2000.505716
```

3. You can continue a calculation using the result of the last calculation. For example, if the final amount determined above is to be divided among seven people, how much would each person get?

   To divide the last calculated amount by seven, press ÷ 7, followed by [ENTER].

   As soon as you press ÷, **Ans/** is displayed at the beginning of the new expression. **Ans** is a variable that contains the last calculated result. In this case, **Ans** contained 2000.505716.

```
       1790.847697
1000*1.06^12
       2012.196472
1000*1.06^11.9
       2000.505716
Ans/7
        285.7865309
```

Graphing Features

The keys on the TI-81 that are related most closely to graphing are located immediately under the display. In the rest of the Getting Started section, you will use all of these keys to graph and explore the behavior of a pair of functions.

Graphing Keys

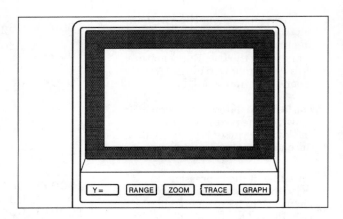

Y= Key

When you press Y= , an edit screen is displayed where you enter and select the functions that you want to graph.

RANGE Key

When you press RANGE , an edit screen is displayed where you define the viewing rectangle for the graph.

ZOOM Key

When you press ZOOM , you access a menu of instructions that allow you to change the viewing rectangle.

TRACE Key

When you press TRACE , you can move the cursor along a graphed function and display the X and Y coordinate values of the cursor location on the function.

GRAPH Key

When you press GRAPH , a graph of the currently selected functions is displayed in the chosen viewing rectangle.

Defining Functions to Graph

Solve the equation $X^3 - 2X = 2\cos X$ graphically using the TI–81. Stated another way, solve the system of two equations and two unknowns: $Y = X^3 - 2X$ and $Y = 2\cos X$.

1. The Y= edit screen allows you to define functions to be graphed. Press $\boxed{Y=}$ to access this edit screen.

   The display shows labels for four functions. The cursor is positioned at the beginning of the first function.

```
: Y1=
: Y2=
: Y3=
: Y4=
```

2. To define the function Y1 in terms of X, enter the first expression, $X^3 - 2X$, by pressing $\boxed{X|T}$ $\boxed{\wedge}$ 3 $\boxed{-}$ 2 $\boxed{X|T}$. Press $\boxed{ENTER}$ to move the cursor to the next function.

   The $\boxed{X|T}$ key lets you enter the X variable quickly without pressing $\boxed{ALPHA}$.

   The = sign is highlighted to show that Y1 is "selected" to be graphed.

```
: Y1█X^3-2X
: Y2=
: Y3=
: Y4=
```

3. To define the function Y2 in terms of X, enter the expression 2cosX by pressing 2 $\boxed{COS}$ $\boxed{X|T}$.

```
: Y1█X^3-2X
: Y2█2cos X
: Y3=
: Y4=
```

Checking the Viewing Rectangle

The viewing rectangle defines the portion of the coordinate plane that appears in the display. The values of the RANGE variables determine the size of the viewing rectangle. You can view and change the values of the RANGE variables.

1. Press RANGE to display the RANGE variables edit screen. You view and edit the values of the RANGE variables on this screen.

   The values shown on the RANGE edit screen are the standard default values.

```
RANGE
Xmin=-10
Xmax=10
Xscl=1
Ymin=-10
Ymax=10
Yscl=1
Xres=1
```

2. The standard default RANGE variables define the viewing rectangle as shown.

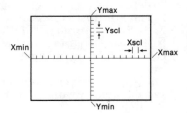

Displaying the Graph

Now that you have created and selected the functions that you want to graph and determined that you want the standard viewing rectangle, you can display the graph.

1. Press GRAPH to graph the selected functions in the viewing rectangle.

   The graph of the functions Y = X^3 − 2X and Y = 2cosX for −10 ≤ X ≤ 10 is shown in the display.

   The display shows that there are two areas that may contain solutions (points where the two functions appear to intersect).

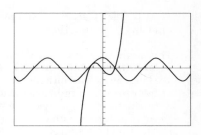

2. Press ► once to display the graphics cursor just to the right of the center of the screen. The bottom line in the display shows the X and Y coordinate values for the position of the graphics cursor.

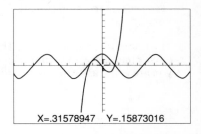

X=.31578947   Y=.15873016

3. Using the cursor-movement keys (◄, ►, ▲, and ▼), move the cursor until it is positioned at the apparent intersection of the two functions on the right side of the display.

   As you move the cursor, the X and Y coordinate values are updated continually with the cursor position.

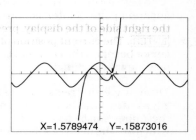

X=1.5789474   Y=.15873016

Zooming In on the Graph

You can magnify the viewing rectangle around a specific
location by selecting the ⟨Zoom In⟩ instruction from the
ZOOM menu.

1. Press ZOOM to access the menu of
   built-in ZOOM functions.

   This menu is typical of all the menus
   of built-in operations on the TI–81.
   To select an item from a menu,
   either press the number to the left
   of the instruction you want, or press
   ▼ to position the cursor on that
   instruction and then press ENTER.

   ```
   ZOOM
   1:Box
   2:Zoom In
   3:Zoom Out
   4:Set Factors
   5:Square
   6:Standard
   7↓Trig
   ```

2. To zoom in, press 2 to select the
   ⟨Zoom In⟩ instruction from the
   menu.

   The graph is displayed again. The
   cursor has changed to indicate that
   you are using a ZOOM instruction.

   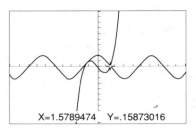

3. With the cursor positioned at the
   apparent point of intersection on
   the right side of the display, press
   ENTER. The current position of the
   cursor becomes the center of the
   new viewing rectangle.

   The new viewing rectangle has been
   adjusted in both the X direction and
   the Y direction by factors of 4,
   which are the default values for the
   zoom factors.

   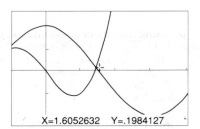

Moving between the Graph and Range Screens

When the TI-81 executes a ZOOM instruction, it updates the RANGE variables to reflect the new viewing rectangle. You can check the RANGE values to see the size of the new viewing rectangle and then return to the graph without having to replot the graph.

1. When you zoom in on the graph, a new viewing rectangle is defined, and the RANGE variables are updated automatically.

   Press RANGE to view the updated values of the RANGE variables.

   Notice the modified values resulting from the ⟨Zoom In⟩ instruction. Depending on the exact cursor position when you executed the ⟨Zoom In⟩ instruction, the RANGE variables on your display may be different.

```
RANGE
Xmin=-.921052632
Xmax=4.078947368
Xscl=1
Ymin=-2.34126984
Ymax=2.658730159
Yscl=1
Xres=1
```

2. Press GRAPH to see the graph again.

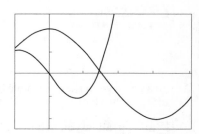

Moving the Cursor along a Function

The TRACE feature allows you to move the cursor along a function, showing the X and Y coordinate values of the cursor location on the function.

1. Press TRACE. The cursor appears near the middle of the screen on the $Y = X^3 - 2X$ function.

   The coordinate values of the cursor location are displayed at the bottom of the screen. The Y value shown is the calculated value of the function for the displayed value of X.

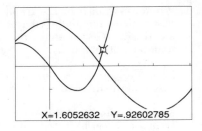

2. Press ▼. The cursor moves to the other function at the same X value where it was located on the first function.

   ▲ and ▼ allow you to move between functions.

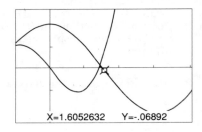

3. Press ▶ several times to move the cursor to the right.

   ▶ and ◀ allow you to move along a function.

4. Press ◄ several times until the
   cursor is positioned on the point of
   intersection between the two
   functions in the first quadrant.

   You see from the graph that the two
   functions do intersect; therefore,
   you have found one solution to the
   equation $X^3 - 2X = 2\cos X$. This
   solution is $X = 1.4473684$, within an
   accuracy of one display dot width
   (0.0526316).

   The width of a display dot is

   $$\frac{(X\max - X\min)}{95}$$

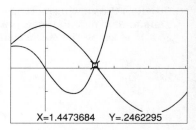

X=1.4473684   Y=.2462295

Using Zoom Box

You have estimated one solution to the equation. Now determine if the other apparent intersection also is a solution. The Zoom ⟨Box⟩ instruction lets you adjust the viewing rectangle by drawing a box on the display to define the new viewing rectangle.

1. To adjust the viewing rectangle to the standard default range, press ZOOM to access the ZOOM menu.

```
ZOOM
1:Box
2:Zoom In
3:Zoom Out
4:Set Factors
5:Square
6:Standard
7↓Trig
```

2. Press 6 to select ⟨Standard⟩. This automatically adjusts the viewing rectangle to the standard default range. This display shows the same graph that you saw earlier.

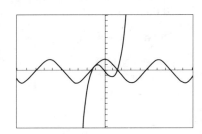

3. Press ZOOM to display the ZOOM menu again. Press 1 to select ⟨Box⟩. This lets you specify two diagonal corners of a new viewing rectangle.

The cursor is in the middle of the screen. Its new appearance indicates that you have selected a ZOOM instruction.

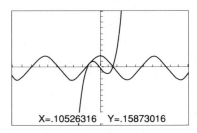

X=.10526316   Y=.15873016

4. Move the cursor from the middle of the graph to where you want one corner of the new viewing rectangle to be. Press ENTER.

   Notice that the cursor has changed to a small box.

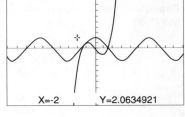
X=-2   Y=2.0634921

5. Move the cursor to the diagonal corner of the desired viewing rectangle.

   The outline of the new viewing rectangle is drawn as you move the cursor.

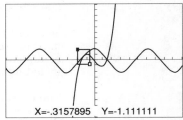
X=-.3157895   Y=-1.111111

6. Press ENTER to accept the cursor location as the second corner of the box.

   The graph is replotted immediately using the box outline as the new viewing rectangle.

7. Repeat steps 3 through 6 until you see that the two functions do not intersect. Thus, there is only one solution to the equation $X^3 - 2X = 2\cos X$.

8. To leave the graph display, press 2nd [QUIT] to return to the Home screen.

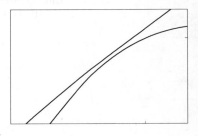

Other Features

This Getting Started section introduced you to basic calculator operation and the function graphing features, including ZOOM and TRACE capabilities. The remainder of this manual describes these features in more detail and also covers the other capabilities of the TI-81.

Other Capabilities of the TI-81

In addition to the features demonstrated in the Getting Started section, other features of the TI-81 are described below.

- Parametric graphing allows you to save, graph, and analyze up to three parametric equations using all of the ZOOM and TRACE features. (See Chapter 4.)

- Drawing and shading features allow you to add emphasis or perform additional analysis on a graph. (See Chapter 5.)

- You can enter and save up to three matrices with maximum dimensions of 6×6. These matrices can be manipulated with standard matrix operations, including elementary row operations. (See Chapter 6.)

- The TI-81 performs one- and two- variable statistical analyses. You can enter and save up to 150 data points. Four regression models are available: linear, logarithmic, exponential, and power models. You can analyze data graphically with histograms, scatter plots, and line drawings and combine them with other graphing capabilities to plot regression equation graphs. (See Chapter 7.)

- Programming capabilities include extensive control and I/O instructions. You can save up to 37 programs in a total of 2400 bytes. (See Chapter 8.)

Chapter 1: Operating the TI-81

This chapter describes the TI-81 and provides general information about its operation.

Chapter Contents

The Keyboard

The keys on the TI-81 keyboard are divided into four zones: graphing keys, editing keys, advanced function keys, and scientific calculator keys.

The Zones of the Keyboard

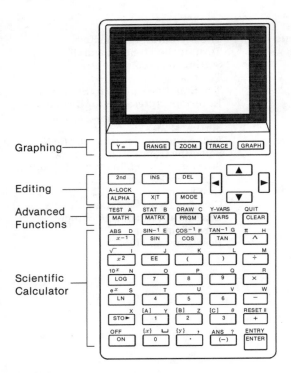

Graphing

Editing

Advanced Functions

Scientific Calculator

Graphing Keys   These keys are most frequently used to access the interactive graphing features of the TI-81.

Editing Keys   These keys are most frequently used for editing expressions and values.

Advanced Function Keys   These keys are used to access the advanced functions of the TI-81.

Scientific Calculator Keys   These keys are used to access the capabilities of a standard scientific calculator.

The Second and Alpha Keys

Some of the keys provide access to more than one function. These additional functions are printed above the keys and are accessed by first pressing the 2nd or ALPHA key.

Key Labels

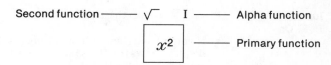

Second function ——— √   I ——— Alpha function

x^2 ——— Primary function

Second Functions

The operation printed to the left above a key is accessed by first pressing and releasing the 2nd key and then pressing the appropriate key.

When you press the 2nd key, the cursor changes to a blinking up-arrow to indicate that the next keystroke is a second function. You can cancel second by pressing 2nd again.

In this manual, second functions are shown in brackets and preceded by the 2nd key symbol; for example, 2nd [√].

Alphabetical Characters

The letter or symbol printed to the right above a key is accessed by first pressing and releasing the ALPHA key and then pressing the appropriate key.

When you press the ALPHA key, the cursor changes to a blinking A to indicate that the next keystroke is an alphabetical character. You can cancel alpha by pressing ALPHA again.

In this manual, alphabetical characters are shown in brackets and preceded by the ALPHA key symbol; for example, ALPHA [I].

Alpha-Lock

You can press 2nd [A-LOCK] to set alpha-lock, which makes each subsequent key press an alpha character. This is useful when entering display text in programs, for example, so that you will not need to press ALPHA before every letter. Cancel alpha-lock by pressing the ALPHA key.

Turning the TI-81 On and Off

To turn the TI-81 on, press the $\boxed{\text{ON}}$ key. To turn the TI-81 off, press $\boxed{\text{2nd}}$ [OFF]. After about five minutes without any activity, the APD™ Automatic Power Down feature turns the TI-81 off automatically.

Turning the TI-81 On

Press $\boxed{\text{ON}}$ to turn the TI-81 on.

- If you turned the TI-81 off by pressing $\boxed{\text{2nd}}$ [OFF], the display shows the Home screen with the cursor in the top left corner (see page 1-6).

- If the APD™ feature turned the calculator off, the TI-81, including the display, cursor, and any error conditions, will be exactly as you left it.

Turning the TI-81 Off

Before turning the TI-81 off, be certain that you have saved any expressions or values that you want to recall later.

To turn the TI-81 off, press $\boxed{\text{2nd}}$ [OFF].

- The display is cleared.

- Any error condition is cleared.

- Stored variables, programs, MODE settings, RANGE variables, contrast setting, Last Answer, Last Entry, and the most recent graph are retained in memory by the Constant Memory™ feature.

The APD™ Automatic Power Down Feature

To prolong the life of the batteries, the APD feature turns the TI-81 off automatically after about five minutes without any activity. When you press $\boxed{\text{ON}}$, the TI-81 will be exactly as you left it.

- The display, cursor, and any error conditions are exactly as you left them.

- Stored variables, contrast setting, Last Answer, Last Entry, programs, MODE settings, RANGE variables, and the most recent graph are retained in memory.

Setting the Display Contrast

The brightness and contrast of the display depend on room lighting, battery freshness, viewing angle, and adjustment of the display contrast. The contrast setting is retained in memory when the TI-81 is turned off.

Adjusting the Display Contrast

You can adjust the display contrast to suit your viewing angle and lighting conditions at any time. As you change the contrast setting, the display contrast changes, and a number in the upper right corner between 0 (lightest) and 9 (darkest) indicates the current contrast setting.

To adjust the contrast:

1. Press and release the 2nd key.

2. Use one of two keys:

   • To increase the contrast to the setting that you want, press and hold ▲.

   • To decrease the contrast to the setting that you want, press and hold ▼.

Caution: If you adjust the contrast setting to zero, the display may become completely blank. If this happens, press and release 2nd and then press and hold ▲ until the display reappears.

When to Replace Batteries

When the batteries are low, the display begins to dim (especially during calculations), and you must adjust the contrast to a higher setting. If you find it necessary to set the contrast to a setting of 8 or 9, you should replace the batteries soon.

The Display

The TI–81 displays both text and graphs. When text is displayed, the screen can display up to eight lines of 16 characters per line. When all eight lines of the screen are filled, text "scrolls" off the top of the screen.

The Home Screen When you turn the TI–81 on, the Home screen is displayed. The Home screen is the primary screen of the TI–81. On it you enter expressions and instructions and see the results.

```
17*3+ln 3 ─────────── Expression
    52.09861229────── Result
```

Display Cursors The TI–81 has several special cursors. In most cases, the appearance of the cursor indicates what will happen when you press the next key.

The cursors that you see on the Home screen are described here. Other special cursors are described in the appropriate chapters.

Cursor	Appearance	Meaning
Entry cursor	Solid blinking rectangle	The next keystroke is entered at the cursor, overwriting any character
Insert cursor	Blinking underline	The next keystroke is inserted at the cursor
2nd cursor	Blinking ↑	The next keystroke is a second function
ALPHA cursor	Blinking **A**	The next keystroke is an alpha character

Busy Indicator When the TI–81 is calculating or graphing, a box in the upper right of the screen is highlighted.

Returning to the Home Screen You can return to the Home screen from any other screen by pressing 2nd [QUIT].

Menu Screens   You can access functions and operations that are not on the keyboard through menus. Menu screens temporarily replace the screen where you are working. After you select an item from a menu, the screen where you are working is displayed again. Using menus is described on pages 1–18 and 1–19.

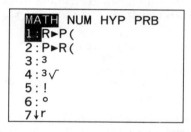

Graph Screens   The graph screen displays a graph of selected functions and the cursor coordinate values.

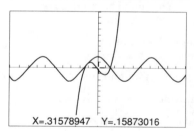

Editing Screens   There are several editing screens that are used to enter or edit expressions or values.

- Statistical data
- Matrix values
- Functions in the Y= list for graphing
- RANGE variables for the viewing rectangle
- Zoom factors for exploring graphs
- Programs

The Equation Operating System

The Equation Operating System (EOS) allows numbers and operations to be entered into the TI-81 in a simple, straightforward sequence. EOS evaluates expressions according to the standard priorities of mathematical operations and uses parentheses for grouping.

Order of Evaluation

EOS evaluates operations in an expression in the following order:

- Polar/rectangular conversions, numerical derivative, round, and row operations.

- Math operations and functions that are entered after the argument, such as x^2, x^{-1}, x^3, $x!$, $^\circ$, ^{r}, and transpose.

- Universal powers, such as $\wedge$.

- Implied multiplication where the second argument is a number, a variable, or a matrix, such as 2π, $4B$, $3[C]$, or $\sin(A+B)4$.

- Math and trig functions that are entered before the argument, such as negation, sine, cosine, tangent, and their inverses, log and antilog, natural log and antilog, absolute value, square root, greatest integer, integer part, fractional part, cube root, determinant, and hyperbolic functions.

- Implied multiplication other than above, such as $3\log 4$ or $\sin 4(A+B)$.

- Permutations and combinations (nPr and nCr).

- Multiplication and division.

- Addition and subtraction.

- Relational operators, such as $>$ or $\leqslant$.

Within a priority group, EOS evaluates operations from left to right. If an expression contains two or more single-argument functions that precede the same argument, EOS evaluates them from right to left. Calculations inside a pair of parentheses are evaluated first.

When you press $\boxed{\text{ENTER}}$, regardless of the cursor location, the expression is completed; the cursor does not need to be at the end of the expression.

Implied Multiplication	When a number precedes a variable, matrix, math or trig function, left parenthesis, or π, it is not necessary to enter the multiplication sign. The TI–81 understands 2π, 4sin 45, $5(1+2)$, $(2*5)(7-4)$, or AB, for example, as implied multiplication. See the previous page for how the TI–81 evaluates implied multiplication.
Using Parentheses	All calculations inside a pair of parentheses are done first. Then the result of that calculation is used to continue the evaluation.
	For example, in the expression $(1+2)4$, the TI–81 first evaluates the portion of the expression inside the parentheses, $1+2$, and then multiplies the result, 3, by 4.
	You may omit any right (close) parenthesis at the end of an expression. All "open" parenthetical elements are closed automatically at the end of the expression when you press ENTER. For clarity, however, all close parentheses are shown in this manual.
Entering a Negative Number	To enter a negative number, use the negation function. Press (−), and then enter the number.
	For example, press (−) 1.7 to enter -1.7.
	Note: The − key is used for subtraction. The TI–81 displays the error message **ERROR 06 SYNTAX** for either of the following cases:

- If you press − for a negative number, as in 9 × − 7 ENTER.

- If you press (−) following a number to indicate subtraction, as in 9 (−) 7 ENTER.

Negation	On the TI–81, negation is a function in the fifth group in the EOS heirarchy. Its place in the order of evaluation in an expression occurs according to EOS. Therefore, functions such as squaring are evaluated before negation. The result of $-x^2$ is a negative number; the result of -9^2 is -81. Use parentheses when you want to square a negative number entry, $(-9)^2$.

Entering Expressions for Evaluation

An expression is a complete sequence of numbers, operations, variables, functions, and their arguments that can be evaluated to a single result. On the TI-81, an expression is entered in the same order that it normally is written.

Entering an Expression

You enter numbers, variable names (see page 1-20), symbols, functions, and operations from the keyboard and from menus to create an expression. An expression is completed when you press ENTER, regardless of the cursor location. The entire expression is evaluated according to EOS, and the result is displayed.

Notice that most of the functions and operations on the keyboard and menus are symbols with several characters in them. You must enter the symbol from the keyboard or menu, not spell it out. For example, to calculate the log of 45, you must press LOG 45; you cannot type in the letters LOG. (If you type LOG, the TI-81 interprets the entry as implied multiplication of the variables L, O, and G.)

Example of Entering an Expression

Calculate $3.76 \div (-7.9 + \sqrt{5}) + 2 \log 45$.

Procedure	Keystrokes	Display
Begin expression	3.76 ÷	3.76/
Begin parentheses	[(]	3.76/(
Enter negative 7.9	[(−)] 7.9	3.76/(-7.9
Add square root of 5	+ [2nd] [√] 5	3.76/(-7.9+√5
Complete parentheses	[)]	3.76/(-7.9+√5)
Add 2 log 45	+ 2 [LOG] 45	3.76/(-7.9+√5)+2 log 45
Evaluate expression	[ENTER]	3.76/(-7.9+√5)+2 log 45 2.642575252

Continuing an Expression

You can recall the answer to a calculation as the first entry in the next expression without reentering the value. Simply begin by pressing an operation key. The TI–81 inserts the variable **Ans** (see page 1–22), which contains the last answer, into the expression.

Example of Continuing an Expression

Square the result of the example on the previous page.

Procedure	Keystrokes	Display
Square prior result	x^2	Ans^2
Evaluate expression	ENTER	Ans^2
		6.983203964

Notes about Entering Expressions

Notice the following about entering expressions:

- Sometimes the displayed symbol is not the same as the key symbol, as in x^2, e^x, and $\div$.

- The TI–81 interprets angles in trig functions based on the MODE setting (degrees or radians).

- If an expression is longer than 16 characters, it "wraps" around to the beginning of the next line.

- The result is displayed on the right side of the next line. The result can be up to ten digits with a two-digit exponent. The MODE settings determine the notation format and number of decimal places displayed (see pages 1–14 through 1–16).

Editing Expressions

Expressions can be edited. The cursor-movement keys move the cursor within and between lines. Normal entry types over the character or symbol where the cursor is. The [INS] and [DEL] keys insert or delete characters or symbols.

The Cursor-Movement Keys

The arrow keys in the upper right of the keyboard control the movement of the cursor.

The ◀ and ▶ keys move the cursor within an expression. The cursor stops when it reaches the beginning or end of the expression.

The ▼ and ▲ keys move the cursor between lines.

When you press and hold one of the cursor-movement keys, the cursor movement repeats until you release the key.

The Edit Keys

Key	Meaning
[INS]	Inserts characters or symbols at the blinking underline cursor
[DEL]	Deletes the character or symbol at the blinking cursor
[CLEAR]	Clears (blanks) the entire expression; on the Home screen, it clears the screen
[ENTER]	Completes the expression

When you press [2nd] or [ALPHA] during an insert, the underline cursor changes to an underlined ↑ or **A** cursor.

[CLEAR] is described in more detail on page 1–24.

Inserting in Expressions

To insert a character or symbol in an expression:

1. Use the cursor-movement keys to position the cursor on the character or symbol in front of which you want to insert.

2. Press INS.

   The cursor changes to a blinking underline.

3. Enter the characters or symbols you want to insert.

4. End the insert in one of the following ways:

   • Press INS again.

   • Press a cursor-movement key.

Deleting from Expressions

To delete a character or symbol from an expression:

1. Use the cursor-movement keys to position the cursor on the character or symbol you want to delete.

2. Press DEL.

   The character or symbol is deleted. All the characters of a symbol that is represented by a group of characters (such as **log** or **sin**) are deleted together.

Setting Modes

Modes determine how numbers and graphs are displayed and calculated. MODE settings are retained by the Constant Memory™ feature when the TI–81 is off.

Checking MODE Settings

Press the MODE key to display the MODE settings. The current settings are highlighted. The various MODE settings are described on the following pages.

Setting	Meaning
Norm Sci Eng	Type of notation for display
Float 0123456789	Number of decimal places
Rad Deg	Type of angle measure
Function Param	Function or parametric graphing
Connected Dot	Whether to connect plotted points
Sequence Simul	How to plot selected functions
Grid Off Grid On	Whether to display a graph grid
Rect Polar	Type of graph coordinate display

Changing MODE Settings

To change any of the settings:

1. Use ▼ or ▲ to move the cursor to the row of the setting that you want to change. The setting that the cursor is on blinks.

2. Use ► or ◄ to move the cursor to the setting that you want.

3. Press ENTER to select the blinking setting.

Leaving the MODE Screen

When the MODE settings are as you want them, leave the MODE screen in one of the following ways:

• Select another screen by pressing the appropriate key, such as Y= or GRAPH.

• Press 2nd [QUIT] to return to the Home screen.

Normal, Scientific, or Engineering Notation Display Format

Notation formats affect only how a numeric result is displayed. You can enter a number in any format.

Normal display format is the way in which we usually express numbers, with digits to the left and right of the decimal, as in 12345.67.

Scientific notation expresses numbers in two parts. The significant digits are displayed with one digit to the left of the decimal. The appropriate power of 10 is displayed to the right of E, as in 1.234567E4.

Engineering notation is similar to scientific notation. However, the number may have one, two, or three digits before the decimal, and the power-of-10 exponent is a multiple of three, as in 12.34567E3.

Note: If you select normal display format, but the result cannot be displayed in 10 digits or the absolute value is less than .001, the TI-81 switches to scientific notation for that result only.

Floating or Fixed Decimal Display Setting

Decimal settings affect only how a result is displayed. They apply to all three notation display formats.

Floating decimal setting displays up to 10 digits, plus the sign and decimal.

Fixed decimal setting displays the selected number of digits to the right of the decimal. Place the cursor on the number of decimal digits you want and then press ENTER.

Radians or Degrees Angle Setting

Radian setting means that angle arguments in trig functions or polar/rectangular conversions are interpreted as radians. Results display in radians.

Degree setting means that angle arguments in trig functions or polar/rectangular conversions are interpreted as degrees. Results display in degrees.

Function or Parametric Graphing Setting

Function graphing plots a function where Y is expressed in terms of X. See Chapter 3 for more information about function graphing.

Parametric graphing plots a relation where X and Y are each expressed in terms of a third variable, T. See Chapter 4 for more information about graphing parametric equations.

Connected Line or Dot Graph Display

A connected line graph draws a line between the points calculated on the graph of a function in the Y= list.

A dot graph plots only the calculated points on the graph.

Sequential or Simultaneous Plotting

Sequential plotting means that, if more than one function is selected, one function is evaluated and plotted completely before the next function is evaluated and plotted.

Simultaneous plotting means that, if more than one function is selected, all functions are evaluated and plotted for a single value of X or T before the functions are evaluated and plotted for the next value of X or T.

Grid Off or Grid On

Grid Off means that no grid points are displayed on a graph.

Grid On means that grid points are displayed on a graph. Grid points correspond to the axis tick marks.

Rectangular or Polar Coordinate Display Setting

Rectangular coordinate display shows the cursor coordinate at the bottom of the screen in terms of rectangular coordinates X and Y.

Polar coordinate display shows the cursor coordinate at the bottom of the screen in terms of polar coordinates R and θ.

Entering Numbers in Scientific Notation

Regardless of the MODE setting, numbers can be entered in the most convenient format. Scientific notation uses the EE key to enter the exponent (the power of 10).

Scientific Notation Entries

To enter a number in scientific notation:

1. If the number is negative, press [(−)].

2. Type the part of the number that precedes the exponent. This value can be an expression.

3. Press [EE].

   E appears in the expression.

4. If the exponent is negative, press [(−)].

5. Type the exponent, which can be one or two digits.

Entering a number in scientific notation does not cause the results to be displayed in scientific or engineering notation.

Example of Entering a Number in Scientific Notation

Enter − .000001234 in scientific notation.

Procedure	Keystrokes	Display
Enter the value	[(−)] .1234	− .1234
Enter the exponent	[EE] [(−)] 5	− .1234E−5

Note: If you enter the above on a blank line on the Home screen and then press [ENTER], the result displayed using default mode settings is $-1.234\text{E}-6$.

Selecting from a Menu

In addition to the alternate functions accessed by pressing
[2nd] or [ALPHA], menus in the display provide access to other
operations. Using specific menus is described in the
appropriate chapters.

The Menu Keys

Keys	Meaning
[ZOOM]	Accesses graphing zoom features
[MATH]	Accesses additional math functions
[MATRX]	Accesses matrix functions and values
[PRGM]	Edits, executes, and erases programs
[VARS]	Accesses special variables
[2nd] [TEST]	Accesses relational operators
[2nd] [STAT]	Accesses statistical features
[2nd] [DRAW]	Accesses graph draw instructions
[2nd] [Y-VARS]	Accesses names of functions in Y= list
[2nd] [RESET]	Resets all values in memory

Leaving a Menu

You can leave a menu without making a selection in one
of the following ways:

- Press a menu key to display a different menu.

- Press [2nd] [QUIT] to return to the Home screen.

- Press [CLEAR] to return to the screen where you were.

The Menu Screen   When you press a menu key, that menu is displayed. For example, if you press $\boxed{\text{MATH}}$, this menu is displayed:

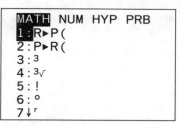

```
MATH NUM HYP PRB
1:R▸P(
2:P▸R(
3:³
4:³√
5:!
6:°
7↓ʳ
```

Moving from One Menu to Another   A menu key may access more than one menu. The names of the menus appear on the top line. The current menu is highlighted and the items in that menu are displayed. Use $\boxed{\blacktriangleright}$ or $\boxed{\blacktriangleleft}$ to move the cursor to a different menu.

Selecting an Item from a Menu   The number of the current item is highlighted. If there are more than seven items on the menu, a ↓ appears on the last line in place of the : (colon). In this manual, menu selections are shown as ⟨item⟩. There are two methods of selecting from a menu.

- Press the number of the item you want to select.

- Use $\boxed{\blacktriangledown}$ and $\boxed{\blacktriangle}$ to move the cursor to the item you want to select and then press $\boxed{\text{ENTER}}$.

Using a Menu Item in an Expression   Calculate $6\sqrt[3]{27}$.

Procedure	Keystrokes	Display
Begin entry	6	6
Access MATH menu	$\boxed{\text{MATH}}$	
Select cube root	4	6³√
Enter 27	27	6³√27
Evaluate expression	$\boxed{\text{ENTER}}$	6³√27
		18

Storing and Recalling Variable Values

Values can be stored to and recalled from memory by using variables. A variable is a name that refers to a location in memory where a value is stored. The variable name represents the value in an expression.

Variables

With the TI–81, variables are represented as single alphabetical characters A through Z, plus θ. In addition, you can reference other variables related to specific applications. These variables are described in the appropriate chapters.

Note: The TI–81 may update the variables X, Y, T, R, or θ when plotting a graph or when you move the cursor on a graph.

Storing Values in Variables

Values are stored to variables with the $\boxed{\text{STO}\blacktriangleright}$ key. To store a value, begin on a blank line.

1. Enter the value you want to store. This value can be an expression, which will be evaluated when you press $\boxed{\text{ENTER}}$.

2. Press $\boxed{\text{STO}\blacktriangleright}$.

   The instruction → is copied to the current cursor location.

3. Press the letter of the variable in which you want to store the value.

   Note: After you press the $\boxed{\text{STO}\blacktriangleright}$ key, the TI–81 keyboard is set for alphabetical entries; therefore, do not press $\boxed{\text{ALPHA}}$ before pressing the letter key.

4. Press $\boxed{\text{ENTER}}$ to complete the instruction.

If you entered an expression, the expression is evaluated and the TI–81 stores the value in the variable.

Displaying the Value of a Variable

To display the value of a variable, begin on a blank line on the Home screen.

1. Enter the name of the variable. (Remember to press ALPHA before entering alphabetical characters.)

2. Press ENTER.

The value of the variable is displayed.

Using Variables in Expressions

Once you have stored a value to a variable, you can use that variable to recall the value. Simply enter the name of the variable in an expression.

To use a variable in an expression, press ALPHA and then the letter. The name of the variable is entered in the expression. When the expression is evaluated, the current value of that variable is used.

Note: The X|T key allows you to enter the variable X in Function mode or T in Parametric mode without pressing ALPHA first.

Storing and Recalling a Value from a Variable

Store the result obtained by adding 10 to 25 in the variable K. Then divide 75 by the result (K).

Procedure	Keystrokes	Display
Enter expression	10 + 25	10+25
Store value in K	STO► [K] ENTER	10+25→K 35
Begin expression	75	75
Divide by K	÷ ALPHA [K]	75/K
Evaluate expression	ENTER	75/K 2.142857143

Last Answer

Whenever an expression is evaluated successfully from the
Home screen or from a program, the TI-81 stores the result in
a special variable, Ans (Last Answer). The variable Ans is
accessed by pressing 2nd [ANS].

**Using Last
Answer**

The **Ans** variable can be used in any operation where a
variable can be used. Press 2nd [ANS] and the variable
name **Ans** appears at the current location of the cursor.
When you press the ENTER key or when the program is
executed, the TI-81 uses the value of **Ans** in the
calculation.

Last Answer can be a value or a matrix.

When you turn the TI-81 off, the value in **Ans** is retained
in memory.

**Using Last
Answer in Place
of Parentheses**

Rework the example on page 1-10:

$3.76 \div (-7.9 + \sqrt{5}) + 2\log 45$.

This time, however, evaluate the portion in parentheses
as a separate expression and then recall it as **Ans** in the
full expression.

Procedure	Keystrokes	Display
Enter negative 7.9	(−) 7.9	−7.9
Add square root of 5	+ 2nd [√] 5	−7.9+√5
Evaluate expression	ENTER	−7.9+√5 −5.663932023
Begin expression	3.76	3.76
Divide by **Ans**	÷ 2nd [ANS]	3.76/Ans
Add 2log 45	+ 2 LOG 45	3.76/Ans+2log 45
Evaluate expression	ENTER	3.76/Ans+2log 45 2.642575252

Last Entry

When ENTER is pressed on the Home screen and an expression is evaluated successfully, the TI-81 stores the current expression in a special storage area called Last Entry. It can be recalled by pressing [2nd] [ENTRY].

Using Last Entry

You can recall the previous expression and edit it. Press [2nd] [ENTRY] to recall the last expression.

Note: If you have not pressed any other key, you can press [▲] to recall the last expression.

Because the TI-81 updates the Last Entry storage area only when ENTER is pressed, you can recall the last entry even if you have begun entering the next expression. However, recalling the Last Entry overwrites the current expression.

When you turn the TI-81 off, the expression in Last Entry is retained in memory.

Pressing ENTER on a blank line on the Home screen executes the expression in Last Entry.

Performing Iterative Calculations with Last Entry

Using the equation $A = \pi r^2$, find by trial and error the radius of a circle that covers 200 square inches. Use 8 as your first guess.

Procedure	Keystrokes	Display
Enter π	[2nd] [π]	π
Multiply by 8^2	8 [x²]	$\pi 8^2$
Evaluate expression	ENTER	$\pi 8^2$
		201.0619298
Recall Last Entry	[2nd] [ENTRY]	$\pi 8^2$
Change 8 to 7	[◄] [◄] 7	$\pi 7^2$
Insert .95	[INS] .95	$\pi 7.95^2$
Evaluate expression	ENTER	$\pi 7.95^2$
		198.5565097

Continue until the result is as accurate as you want.

Clearing Expressions and Entries

Depending on the screen, the $\boxed{\text{CLEAR}}$ key can be used to clear a value, an expression, or the Home screen. Specific uses of $\boxed{\text{CLEAR}}$ are described in the appropriate chapters.

Clearing a Value

There are several screens on which you can press the $\boxed{\text{CLEAR}}$ key to clear (blank) a value. Pressing $\boxed{\text{CLEAR}}$ on an edit screen blanks the value; it does not store a zero.

- Press $\boxed{\text{CLEAR}}$ to clear a value in a statistical data entry.

- Press $\boxed{\text{CLEAR}}$ to clear a value in a matrix.

- Press $\boxed{\text{CLEAR}}$ to clear the value of a RANGE variable.

- Press $\boxed{\text{CLEAR}}$ to clear the value of a zoom factor.

Clearing an Expression

There are several screens where you can press the $\boxed{\text{CLEAR}}$ key to clear (blank) an expression so that you can enter a new expression.

- Press $\boxed{\text{CLEAR}}$ to clear an expression on the program edit screen.

- Press $\boxed{\text{CLEAR}}$ to clear the current function on the Y= edit screen.

Clearing the Home Screen

Press $\boxed{\text{CLEAR}}$ to clear everything on the Home screen.

Using $\boxed{\text{CLEAR}}$ to Cancel a Menu

To leave a menu and return to the screen where you were, press $\boxed{\text{CLEAR}}$ to cancel the current menu.

Leaving a Menu or Edit Screen

There are several ways to leave a menu or edit screen.

Leaving a Menu

After you make a selection from a menu, you usually are returned to the screen where you were. If you decide not to make a selection from a menu, you can leave the menu in one of the following ways:

- Press 2nd [QUIT] to return to the Home screen.

- Press CLEAR to return to the screen where you were.

- Select another screen by pressing the appropriate key, such as MATH or RANGE.

Leaving an Edit Screen

When you finish entry or editing tasks, such as entering statistical data, editing a program, or changing modes, leave the menu in one of the following ways:

- Press 2nd [QUIT] to return to the Home screen.

- Press another edit screen key, such as RANGE.

Error Conditions

The TI–81 detects an error when it evaluates an expression, executes an instruction, plots a graph, or stores a value. Calculations stop and an error message with a menu displays immediately.

Diagnosing Errors

When the TI–81 detects an error, it displays this special menu:

```
ERROR nn type
1:Goto Error
2:Quit
```

The error message on the top line indicates an error number and the type of error: **MATH**, **RANGE**, **ZOOM**, **BREAK**, **PRGM**, **SYNTAX**, **MEMORY**, or **INVALID**.

- If you select ⟨Goto Error⟩, the cursor appears at the location where the error was detected.

- If you select ⟨Quit⟩ or press CLEAR, you go to the Home screen.

Note: Some errors do not have the ⟨Goto Error⟩ option on the menu.

Errors are described in detail in Appendix B, but you should look for the following common types of errors:

- Use of the [(−)] key instead of the [−] key or vice versa

- Missing or mismatched parentheses

- Improperly placed arguments

Correcting an Error

To correct an error:

1. Note the number and type of the error.

2. Press ⊡1⊡ to go to the error, if that option is available.

3. Look at the expression, especially at the location of the cursor, for syntax errors or one of the common errors described on the previous page.

   If the error in the expression is not readily apparent, turn to Appendix B and read the information about the error message.

4. Correct the error:

   • If the error occurred because of an error in entering the expression, use the editing keys to correct the expression.

   • If the error occurred because of an error in values or logic, make the appropriate correction.

5. Press ENTER to re-evaluate the expression or return to the Home screen and re-execute the program.

Resetting the TI-81

Resetting the TI-81 restores the memory to the factory settings. Because there are operations that clear only selected portions of memory, the TI-81 should be reset only under special circumstances, such as when it is first acquired.

Resetting the TI-81

1. Press 2nd [RESET]. The RESET menu appears. Information is displayed about the amount of memory currently used and available for use by programs and statistical data.

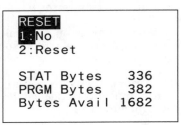

```
RESET
1:No
2:Reset

STAT Bytes    336
PRGM Bytes    382
Bytes Avail  1682
```

2. Make the appropriate menu selection:

   • If you do not want to reset the TI-81, press 1 to select ⟨No⟩. You are returned to the screen where you were.

   • If you want to reset the TI-81, press 2 to select ⟨Reset⟩. The calculator is reset and the message **Mem cleared** is displayed.

Results of Resetting

When you reset the TI-81:

• The contrast setting is set to the default.
• The MODE settings are set to the defaults.
• The viewing rectangle is set to the standard defaults.
• All variable values are set to zero.
• All statistical data is erased.
• All matrix values are set to zero.
• All matrix dimensions are set to 6 by 6.
• All functions in the Y= list are erased.
• All programs are erased.
• Zoom factors are set to 4.
• Rand is reset to the factory seed of 0.

Chapter 2: Math and Test Operations

This chapter describes math and relational operations that are available on the TI-81. The most commonly used math functions are accessed from the keyboard; others are accessed through the MATH menu. Relational operators are accessed through the TEST menu.

The Keyboard Math Functions

The most commonly used math operations and functions are on the keyboard. These examples assume that the default MODE settings are in effect.

Operations	Example	Keystrokes	Display
$+, -, \times, \div$	$75 - 12 \times 2$	75 [−] 12 [×] 2 [ENTER]	75−12∗2 51
x^2	6^2	6 [x²] [ENTER]	6^2 36
$\sqrt{x}$	$\sqrt{16}$	[2nd] [√] 16 [ENTER]	√16 4
x^{-1}	$1/4$	4 [x⁻¹] [ENTER]	4^{-1} .25
Powers	2^5	2 [∧] 5 [ENTER]	2^5 32
Roots	$\sqrt[5]{32}$	32 [∧] 5 [x⁻¹] [ENTER]	32^5⁻¹ 2
sin, cos, tan	$\sin \pi$	[SIN] [2nd] [π] [ENTER]	sin π 0
$\sin^{-1}, \cos^{-1},$ and $\tan^{-1}$	$\sin^{-1} 1$	[2nd] [SIN⁻¹] 1 [ENTER]	sin⁻¹ 1 1.570796327
log, ln	$\ln 1$	[LN] 1 [ENTER]	ln 1 0
$10^x, e^x$	e^0	[2nd] [eˣ] 0 [ENTER]	e^0 1
abs	$\lvert -1.2 \rvert$	[2nd] [ABS] [(−)] 1.2 [ENTER]	abs −1.2 1.2

Notes about Keyboard Math Functions

$\sin^{-1}$, $\cos^{-1}$, and $\tan^{-1}$ are the inverse trig functions, arcsin, arccos, and arctan, respectively.

x^{-1}, the multiplicative inverse, is the equivalent of the reciprocal $1/x$.

Raising a negative number to a noninteger power results in a complex number and therefore is not allowed.

Pi

Pi is stored as a constant in the TI–81. You access it by pressing [2nd] [π]. The symbol π appears on the screen; the number 3.14159265359 is used in calculations.

Using the MATH Menus

Pressing [MATH] accesses additional mathematical functions and operations that do not appear on the keyboard. They are grouped functionally into four menus: math, number, hyperbolic, and probability.

The MATH Menus

Menu	Meaning
MATH NUM HYP PRB	
1:R►P(	Rectangular to polar conversion
2:P►R(	Polar to rectangular conversion
3:³	Cube
4:³√	Cube root
5:!	Factorial
6:°	Degree notation
7:ʳ	Radian notation
8:NDeriv(	Numerical derivative
MATH **NUM** HYP PRB	
1:Round(	Round
2:IPart	Integer part
3:FPart	Fractional part
4:Int	Greatest integer
MATH NUM **HYP** PRB	
1:sinh	Hyperbolic sine
2:cosh	Hyperbolic cosine
3:tanh	Hyperbolic tangent
4:sinh⁻¹	Hyperbolic arcsine
5:cosh⁻¹	Hyperbolic arccosine
6:tanh⁻¹	Hyperbolic arctangent
MATH NUM HYP **PRB**	
1:Rand	Random number generator
2: nPr	Number of permutations $P\binom{n}{r}$
3: nCr	Number of combinations $C\binom{n}{r}$

Notes about the MATH Menus

The current menu name and item number are highlighted.

When you select an operation from a MATH menu, the name of the operation is copied to the current cursor location in the expression you are editing.

Leaving the MATH Menus

You can leave the MATH menus without making a selection in one of the following ways:

- Select another screen by pressing the appropriate key, such as [Y=] or [GRAPH].

- Press [2nd] [QUIT] to return to the Home screen.

- Press [CLEAR] to return to the screen where you were.

Using the MATH (Mathematical) Menu

To display the MATH menu, press MATH. These examples assume that the default MODE settings are in effect.

MATH Operation	Example	Keystrokes	Display
1 : R►P (	Convert (X=−1, Y=0) to (R,θ), display R	MATH ⟨R►P(⟩ (−) 1 ALPHA [,] 0 ⟨)⟩	R►P(R►P(−1,0)
		ENTER	1
	Display θ	ALPHA [θ]	θ
		ENTER	3.141592654
2 : P►R (	Convert (R=1, θ = π) to (X,Y), display X	MATH ⟨P►R(⟩ 1 ALPHA [,] 2nd [π] ⟨)⟩	P►R(P►R(1,π)
		ENTER	−1
	Display Y	ALPHA [Y]	Y
		ENTER	0
3 : ³	5³	5 MATH ⟨³⟩	5³
		ENTER	125
4 : ³√	³√125	MATH ⟨³√ ⟩ 125	³√125
		ENTER	5
5 : !	6!	6 MATH ⟨!⟩	6!
		ENTER	720
6 : °	sin 45°	SIN 45 MATH ⟨°⟩	sin 45°
		ENTER	.7071067812
7 : ʳ	sin 2 (in radians)	SIN 2 MATH ⟨ʳ⟩	sin 2ʳ
		ENTER	.9092974268
8 : NDeriv (	Estimate f′(5) where f(X)=X³ and ΔX = .001	5 STO► [X]	5→X
		ENTER	5
		MATH ⟨NDeriv(⟩	NDeriv(
		ALPHA [X] MATH ⟨³⟩	NDeriv(X³
		ALPHA [,] .001 ⟨)⟩	NDeriv(X³,.001)
		ENTER	75.000001

Notes about MATH Menu Operations

The placement of the arguments of each function is described in Appendix A.

R▶P(requires two arguments, separated by a comma. The first is the X-coordinate value and the second is the Y-coordinate value of a point in rectangular coordinates. The function stores the converted coordinate values in the variables R and θ.

P▶R(requires two arguments, separated by a comma. The first is the R-coordinate value and the second is the θ-coordinate value of a point in polar coordinates. The function stores the converted coordinate values in the variables X and Y.

The degree (°) and radian (^{r}) notations let you designate an argument as degree or radian, independent of the current angle MODE setting.

NDeriv(requires two arguments. The first argument is an expression in terms of X. The second argument is a delta X. The numerical derivative value is the slope of the secant line through the points $(X - \Delta X, f(X - \Delta X))$ and $(X + \Delta X, f(X + \Delta X))$ for the current value of X. This is an approximation of the numerical derivative of the function at X. As ΔX gets smaller, the approximation usually gets more accurate.

Using the NUM (Number) Menu

To display the NUM menu, press $\boxed{\text{MATH}}$ $\boxed{\blacktriangleright}$. These examples assume that the default MODE settings are in effect.

NUM Operation	Example	Keystrokes	Display
1:Round(	Round −23.45 to tenths	$\boxed{\text{MATH}}$ $\boxed{\blacktriangleright}$ ⟨Round(⟩ $\boxed{(-)}$ 23.45 $\boxed{\text{ALPHA}}$ [,] 1 $\boxed{)}$ $\boxed{\text{ENTER}}$	Round(-23.45,1) -23.5
2:IPart	Find integer part of −23.45	$\boxed{\text{MATH}}$ $\boxed{\blacktriangleright}$ ⟨IPart⟩ $\boxed{(-)}$ 23.45 $\boxed{\text{ENTER}}$	IPart -23.45 -23
3:FPart	Find fractional part of −23.45	$\boxed{\text{MATH}}$ $\boxed{\blacktriangleright}$ ⟨FPart⟩ $\boxed{(-)}$ 23.45 $\boxed{\text{ENTER}}$	FPart -23.45 -.45
4:Int	Find greatest integer in −23.45	$\boxed{\text{MATH}}$ $\boxed{\blacktriangleright}$ ⟨Int⟩ $\boxed{(-)}$ 23.45 $\boxed{\text{ENTER}}$	Int -23.45 -24

Notes about NUM Menu Operations

The placement of the arguments of each function is described in Appendix A.

Round(can take two arguments. The first argument is the number, variable name, expression, or matrix to be rounded. The second argument is optional. It is the number of decimal places to round to. If the second argument is not specified, the number is rounded to ten digits.

Round(can be used with matrices. Evaluating the expression **Round([A], 0)** ▸ **[A]** changes [A] to an integer matrix.

FPart and **IPart** return the fractional part and integer part, respectively, of the argument.

Int returns the greatest integer contained within the argument. The result is the same as **IPart** for nonnegative numbers and negative integers, but is one integer less than that returned by **IPart** for negative noninteger numbers.

Using the HYP (Hyperbolic) Menu

To display the HYP menu, press [MATH] [▶] [▶]. These examples assume that the default MODE settings are in effect.

HYP Operation	Example	Keystrokes	Display
1:sinh	sinh .5	[MATH] [▶] [▶] ⟨sinh⟩ .5 [ENTER]	sinh .5 .5210953055
2:cosh	cosh .5	[MATH] [▶] [▶] ⟨cosh⟩ .5 [ENTER]	cosh .5 1.127625965
3:tanh	tanh .5	[MATH] [▶] [▶] ⟨tanh⟩ .5 [ENTER]	tanh .5 .4621171573
4:sinh⁻¹	sinh⁻¹ 5	[MATH] [▶] [▶] ⟨sinh⁻¹⟩ 5 [ENTER]	sinh⁻¹ 5 2.312438341
5:cosh⁻¹	cosh⁻¹ 5	[MATH] [▶] [▶] ⟨cosh⁻¹⟩ 5 [ENTER]	cosh⁻¹ 5 2.29243167
6:tanh⁻¹	tanh⁻¹ .5	[MATH] [▶] [▶] ⟨tanh⁻¹⟩ .5 [ENTER]	tanh⁻¹ .5 .5493061443

Notes about HYP Menu Operations   The placement of the argument of each function is described in Appendix A.

sinh⁻¹, cosh⁻¹, and tanh⁻¹ are hyperbolic arcsin, hyperbolic arccos, and hyperbolic arctan, respectively.

Using the PRB (Probability) Menu

To display the PRB menu, press [MATH] [◄]. These examples assume that the default MODE settings are in effect.

PRB Operation	Example	Keystrokes	Display
1 : Rand	3/Rand	3 [÷] [MATH] [◄] ⟨Rand⟩ [ENTER]	3/Rand 3.17932202
2 : nPr	Permutations of 4 items taken 3 at a time	4 [MATH] [◄] ⟨ nPr⟩ 3 [ENTER]	4 nPr 3 24
3 : nCr	Combinations of 4 items taken 3 at a time	4 [MATH] [◄] ⟨ nCr⟩ 3 [ENTER]	4 nCr 3 4

Notes about PRB Menu Operations

The placement of the arguments of each function is described in Appendix A.

Rand generates a number greater than 0 and less than 1. To control a random number sequence, first store an integer seed value in **Rand** for the random number generator. For example, to store 0 to **Rand**, press 0 [STO►] [ALPHA] [MATH] [◄] ⟨Rand⟩ [ENTER]. If you store 0 to **Rand**, the TI–81 uses the factory-set seed value. When you reset the TI–81, **Rand** is set to the factory seed.

The arguments of **nPr** and **nCr** must be nonnegative integers.

Using the TEST (Relational) Menu

Pressing [2nd] [TEST] accesses a menu of relational operators that compare two values or expressions and return a value of 1 if the test is true or 0 if the test is false.

The TEST Menu

Menu	Meaning
TEST	
1 :=	Equal to
2 : ≠	Not equal to
3 : >	Greater than
4 : ≥	Greater than or equal to
5 : <	Less than
6 : ≤	Less than or equal to

Notes about the TEST Menu

The current menu name and item number are highlighted.

When you select an operator from the TEST menu, the name of the operator is copied to the current cursor location in the expression you are editing.

The expression, including the relational operator, is evaluated when you press [ENTER] or when the program is executed. When evaluated, each test compares the values or the evaluated expressions on each side of the operator and returns a value of 1 if true or 0 if false.

Leaving the TEST Menus

You can leave the TEST menus without making a selection in one of the following ways:

- Select another screen by pressing the appropriate key, such as [Y=] or [GRAPH].

- Press [2nd] [QUIT] to return to the Home screen.

- Press [CLEAR] to return to the screen where you were.

Using the Relational Operators

To display the TEST menu, press [2nd] [TEST]. **Before working these examples, store the value 8 into the variable J. These examples assume that the default MODE settings are in effect.**

TEST Operation	Example	Keystrokes	Display
1 : =	Is J = 8?	[ALPHA] [J] [2nd] [TEST] ⟨ = ⟩ 8 [ENTER]	J = 8 1
2 : ≠	Is J≠8?	[ALPHA] [J] [2nd] [TEST] ⟨≠⟩ 8 [ENTER]	J≠8 0
3 : >	Is J>8?	[ALPHA] [J] [2nd] [TEST] ⟨>⟩ 8 [ENTER]	J>8 0
4 : ≥	Is J≥8?	[ALPHA] [J] [2nd] [TEST] ⟨ ≥ ⟩ 8 [ENTER]	J ≥ 8 1
5 : <	Is J<8?	[ALPHA] [J] [2nd] [TEST] ⟨<⟩ 8 [ENTER]	J<8 0
6 : ≤	Is J≤8?	[ALPHA] [J] [2nd] [TEST] ⟨ ≤ ⟩ 8 [ENTER]	J ≤ 8 1

Notes about TEST Menu Operations

The placement of the arguments of each operator is described in Appendix A.

Relational operators are the lowest priority in the EOS evaluation hierarchy.

- The expression **2+2=2+3** evaluates to 0. The TI–81 first performs the addition and then compares 4 to 5.

- The expression **2+(2=2)+3** evaluates to 6. The TI–81 first performs the test because it is in parentheses and then adds 2, 1, and 3.

Tests can be used in programs to control program flow (see page 8–10). Tests also can be used to control the graph of a function over certain values (see page 9–4).

Chapter 3: Function Graphing

This chapter describes function graphing on the TI–81 in detail. It also lays the foundation for using the other graphing features of the TI–81.

Defining a Graph

A graph is defined by setting the modes, entering and selecting functions to be graphed, and setting the viewing rectangle. Once a graph is defined, it can be displayed and explored.

Steps in Defining a Graph

There are four basic steps to defining a graph. You may not need to do all of the steps each time you define a graph. The procedures are described in detail on the following pages.

1. Set the modes appropriate to the graph.

2. Enter or edit an expression to define a function in the Y= list.

3. Select the function or functions in the Y= list that you want to graph.

4. Define the viewing rectangle by entering the RANGE variables.

Once a graph has been defined, you can display it and use several tools of the TI–81 to explore the behavior of the function or functions. These tools are described later in this chapter.

Setting Graph Modes

Pressing $\boxed{\text{MODE}}$ displays the current MODE settings (see pages 1–15 and 1–16). The MODE settings can be changed on the MODE screen (see page 1–14).

Checking Graph Modes

Press $\boxed{\text{MODE}}$ to display the MODE settings. The current settings are highlighted.

To graph functions, you must select ⟨Function⟩. Not all modes affect graph screens. The settings that affect graphs are shown below.

Setting	Meaning
Rad Deg	Type of angle measure
Function Param	Function or parametric graphing
Connected Dot	Whether to connect plotted points
Sequence Simul	How to plot selected functions
Grid Off Grid On	Whether to display a graph grid
Rect Polar	Type of graph coordinate display

Changing Graph Modes

To change any of the MODE settings:

1. Use $\boxed{\blacktriangledown}$ or $\boxed{\blacktriangle}$ to move the cursor to the row of the setting that you want to change. The setting that the cursor is on blinks.

2. Use $\boxed{\blacktriangleright}$ or $\boxed{\blacktriangleleft}$ to move the cursor to the setting that you want.

3. Press $\boxed{\text{ENTER}}$ to select the blinking setting.

Leaving the MODE Screen

When the MODE settings are as you want them, leave the MODE screen in one of the following ways:

- Select another screen by pressing the appropriate key, such as $\boxed{\text{Y=}}$ or $\boxed{\text{GRAPH}}$.

- Press $\boxed{\text{2nd}}$ [QUIT] to return to the Home screen.

Defining Functions in the Y= List

Pressing [Y=] accesses the Y= edit screen where functions to be graphed are entered. Up to four functions can be stored in memory at one time. One or more of these functions can be graphed at a time.

Displaying the Functions in the Y= List

Press [Y=] to display the Y= edit screen. In the example below, only the Y1 function is defined.

```
: Y1█X²+2X+5
: Y2=
: Y3=
: Y4=
```

Entering an Expression to Define a Function

To enter an expression on the Y= edit screen to define a new function:

1. Use [▼] or [▲] to move the cursor to an undefined function.

2. Enter the expression that defines the function in the Y= list.

   • You may use variables, matrix elements, or math and trig functions in the expression.

   • The independent variable in the function must be X. You may press the [X|T] key, rather than pressing [ALPHA] [X], for the X variable. (Function mode defines the independent variable as X.)

   • The expression is stored as one of the four user-defined functions in the Y= list as you enter it.

3. When you complete the expression, press [ENTER] to move to the beginning of the next function.

Editing a Function

To edit an existing function on the Y= edit screen:

1. Use ▼ or ▲ to move the cursor to the function in the Y= list that you want to change.

2. Enter the changes to the function in the Y= list using one of the following methods:

   • Use ▶ or ◀ to position the cursor over the symbol you want to change. Then type over it or use INS or DEL to change it.

   • Press CLEAR to erase the expression and then enter a new expression.

   The expression is stored as one of the four user-defined functions in the Y= list as you enter it.

3. When you complete the expression, press ENTER to move to the beginning of the next function.

Clearing a Function

To clear or erase a function on the Y= edit screen, position the cursor anywhere on the function and then press CLEAR.

Leaving the Y= Edit Screen

When you finish defining functions, leave the Y= edit screen in one of the following ways:

• Select another screen by pressing the appropriate key, such as GRAPH or RANGE.

• Press 2nd [QUIT] to return to the Home screen.

Selecting Functions

Only functions that are selected are graphed. Up to four functions may be selected at one time.

Turning a Function "On" or "Off"

You select and unselect ("turn on" and "turn off") functions on the Y= edit screen. The = sign on a selected function is highlighted.

To change the selection status of a function:

1. If the Y= edit screen is not displayed, press Y= to display the functions.

2. Move the cursor to the function whose status you want to change.

3. Use ◄ to place the cursor over the = sign of the function.

4. Press ENTER to change the status.

5. When you finish selecting functions, leave the Y= edit screen in one of the following ways:

   • Select another screen by pressing the appropriate key, such as GRAPH or RANGE.

   • Press 2nd [QUIT] to return to the Home screen.

Note: When you enter or edit a function, it is selected automatically. When you clear a function, it is unselected.

Defining the Viewing Rectangle

The RANGE variables determine the boundaries and other attributes of the viewing rectangle. The viewing rectangle that the TI–81 displays is the portion of the coordinate plane defined by **Xmin, Xmax, Ymin,** and **Ymax.**

Checking the Viewing Rectangle

Press [RANGE] to display the current RANGE variable values. The values shown are the standard defaults.

RANGE
Xmin=−10
Xmax=10
Xscl=1
Ymin=−10
Ymax=10
Yscl=1
Xres=1

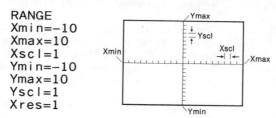

Xres is an integer from 1 to 8 that specifies the plotting resolution. To turn off the tick marks, set **Xscl** or **Yscl** to zero.

Changing the Viewing Rectangle

To change a RANGE variable value:

1. Use [▼] or [▲] to move the cursor to the RANGE variable that you want to change.

2. Enter the new value using one of these methods:

   • Enter a new value. The original value is cleared automatically when you begin typing.

   • Use [▶] or [◀] to position the cursor over the digit you want to change. Then type over it or use [DEL] to delete it.

3. When you have changed the value, press [ENTER]. The cursor moves to the next value.

Note: **Xmin** must be less than **Xmax,** and **Ymin** must be less than **Ymax,** or you will get **ERROR 11 RANGE** when you press [GRAPH].

Leaving the RANGE Edit Screen

When all the variables are as you want them, leave the RANGE edit screen in one of the following ways:

• Select another screen by pressing the appropriate key, such as [GRAPH] or [Y=].

• Press [2nd] [QUIT] to return to the Home screen.

Displaying a Graph

Pressing GRAPH graphs any functions selected on the Y=
edit screen. The current MODE settings apply, and the current
values of the RANGE variables define the viewing rectangle.

**The GRAPH
Screen**

Press GRAPH to display the graph of the selected
function or functions. While the functions are being
graphed, the busy indicator is turned on.

The value of the RANGE variable Xres affects the plotting
speed and resolution of the graph. If Xres is 1, the
function is evaluated and plotted for every dot along the
X axis (96 times); if Xres is 2, it is evaluated and plotted at
alternating dots (48 times), and so on.

As a graph is plotted, the TI–81 updates the variables X
and Y.

Note: While a graph is being plotted, you can press ON
to stop graphing. You must press GRAPH to start over.

**The
"Smart Graph"
Feature**

The "Smart Graph" feature links modes, functions and
their variables, and ranges to the displayed graph. If you
changed one or more of these, pressing GRAPH replots
the graph based on the new values.

If you have not changed any of these since the graph was
last displayed, the "Smart Graph" feature displays the
graph immediately when you press GRAPH.

When you press GRAPH, the "Smart Graph" feature
recalculates and replots the functions if you have done
one or more of the following:

- Changed a MODE setting that affects graphs.

- Changed the function.

- Selected or unselected a function.

- Changed the value stored to a variable that was used
  in a selected function.

- Changed a RANGE value.

- Cleared drawings by selecting ⟨ClrDraw⟩ (see Chapter 5).

Exploring a Graph with the Free-Moving Cursor

While a graph is displayed, the free-moving cursor can be moved anywhere on the graph to identify the coordinate of any location on the graph.

The Free-Moving Cursor

You can use ◄, ►, ▲, and ▼ to move the cursor around the graph. When you first display the graph, no cursor is visible. As soon as you press one of the cursor-movement keys, the cursor moves from the center of the viewing rectangle.

As you move the cursor around the graph, the coordinate values of the cursor location are displayed at the bottom of the screen. Coordinate values generally appear in normal floating-decimal format. The numeric display settings on the MODE screen do not affect coordinate display.

In Rectangular mode, moving the cursor updates and displays the values of the variables X and Y. (In Polar mode, the variables X, Y, R, and θ are updated, and R and θ are displayed.)

To see the graph without the cursor or coordinate values, press GRAPH or ENTER. When you press a cursor-movement key, the cursor moves from the middle of the viewing rectangle again if you pressed GRAPH or from the same point if you pressed ENTER.

Note: The free-moving cursor moves from dot to dot on the screen. When you move the cursor to a dot that appears to be "on" the function, it may be near, but not on, the function; therefore, the coordinate value displayed at the bottom of the screen is not necessarily a point on the function. The coordinate value is accurate to within the width of the dot. To move the cursor along a function, use the TRACE feature (see the following page).

Exploring a Graph with the TRACE Feature

The TRACE feature moves the cursor from one plotted point to the next along a function, while displaying the cursor coordinate at the bottom of the screen.

Beginning a Trace

Press TRACE to begin a trace. If the graph is not displayed already, the TI–81 displays it for you. The blinking cursor is on the first selected function in the Y= list at the middle X value on the screen.

Moving along a Function

Use ▶ or ◀ to move the cursor along the function. Each press of an arrow key moves the cursor from one plotted point to the next. In Rectangular mode, tracing updates and displays the values of the variables X and Y. (In Polar mode, the variables X, Y, R, and θ are updated, and R and θ are displayed.)

The Y value is calculated from the X value. If the function is undefined at an X value, the Y value is blank.

If the Y value of a function is above or below the viewing rectangle, the cursor disappears as you move it to that portion of the function; however, the coordinate values displayed at the bottom of the screen continue to be updated with the cursor coordinate location.

Panning to the Left or Right

If you move the cursor to the edge of the screen while tracing a function that goes off the left or right of the graph (and **Xres** is 1), the viewing rectangle automatically pans to the left or right so that you can continue to view the function. The RANGE variables **Xmin** and **Xmax** are updated to correspond to the new viewing rectangle.

Moving from Function to Function

To trace another selected function on the graph, use ▼ or ▲ to move the cursor to that function. The cursor movement is based on the order of the selected functions in the Y= list, not the appearance of the functions as graphed on the screen. The cursor moves to the new function at the same X value.

Leaving TRACE

When you finish tracing functions, leave TRACE in one of the following ways:

- Select another screen by pressing the appropriate key, such as GRAPH or ZOOM.

- Press 2nd [QUIT] to return to the Home screen.

Exploring a Graph with the ZOOM Features

Pressing [ZOOM] accesses a menu of instructions that adjust the viewing rectangle of the graph.

The ZOOM Menu

Menu	Meaning
ZOOM	
1: Box	Draws box to define viewing rectangle
2: Zoom In	Magnifies graph around cursor
3: Zoom Out	Views more of graph around cursor
4: Set Factors	Changes Zoom-In, Zoom-Out factors
5: Square	Sets equal sized dots on X and Y axes
6: Standard	Sets built-in default RANGE variables
7: Trig	Sets built-in trig RANGE variables
8: Integer	Sets integer values on X and Y axes

Notes about the ZOOM Menu

The current menu name and item number are highlighted.

Box, **Zoom In**, **Zoom Out**, and **Integer** prompt you to move the cursor to further define the new viewing rectangle. **Square**, **Standard**, and **Trig** plot the new graph as soon as you make the menu selection.

You can change the Zoom-In and Zoom-Out factors with **Set Factors**.

When one of these instructions is executed, the TI–81 updates the values of the RANGE variables and displays the graph using the new values.

Using Zoom Box

Zoom Box uses the cursor to select opposite corners of a rectangle. The TI-81 then replots the functions using that rectangle (box) to define the new viewing rectangle.

Defining the Zoom Box

To view a portion of the graph in greater detail:

1. Select ⟨Box⟩ from the ZOOM menu.

   Notice the special cursor at the center of the screen. It indicates that you are using a Zoom instruction.

2. Move the cursor to any corner of the box you want to define. Then press ENTER.

   If you move the cursor away from the point just selected, you see a small square dot, indicating that the first corner is selected.

3. Move the cursor to the diagonal corner of the box you want to define. As you move the cursor, the boundaries of the box change on the screen.

   Note: You can cancel the Zoom Box procedure any time before you press ENTER in one of the following ways:

   • Select another screen by pressing the appropriate key, such as GRAPH or ZOOM.

   • Press 2nd [QUIT] to return to the Home screen.

4. When the box is defined as you want it, press ENTER.

   The TI–81 updates the RANGE variables and replots the functions in the new viewing rectangle defined by the box.

Using Zoom In

Zoom In magnifies the graph around the cursor location. The
XFact and YFact settings determine the extent of the
magnification.

Zooming In on a Graph

1. After checking or changing the zoom factors (see page
   3–15), select ⟨Zoom In⟩ from the ZOOM menu.

   Notice the special cursor. It indicates that you are
   using a Zoom instruction.

2. Move the cursor to the point that you want as the
   center of the new viewing rectangle. Then press
   ENTER.

   The TI–81 adjusts the viewing rectangle by **XFact** and
   YFact, updates the RANGE variables, and replots the
   selected functions, centered around the cursor
   location.

3. To zoom in on the graph again:

   • To zoom in at the same point, press ENTER.

   • To zoom in at a new point, move the cursor to the
     point that you want as the center of the new
     viewing rectangle and then press ENTER.

Leaving Zoom In

When you finish using this feature, leave in one of the
following ways:

   • Select another screen by pressing the appropriate key,
     such as TRACE or GRAPH.

   • Press 2nd [QUIT] to return to the Home screen.

Using Zoom Out

Zoom Out displays a greater portion of the graph, centered around the cursor location, to provide a more global view. The XFact and YFact settings determine the extent of the zoom.

Zooming Out on a Graph

1. After checking or changing the zoom factors (see page 3–15), select ⟨Zoom Out⟩ from the ZOOM menu.

   Notice the special cursor. It indicates that you are using a Zoom instruction.

2. Move the cursor to the point that you want as the center of the new viewing rectangle and then press ENTER.

   The TI–81 adjusts the viewing rectangle by **XFact** and **YFact**, updates the RANGE variables, and replots the selected functions, centered around the cursor location.

3. To zoom out from the graph again:

   • To zoom out at the same point, press ENTER.

   • To zoom out at a new point, move the cursor to the point that you want as the center of the new viewing rectangle and then press ENTER.

Leaving Zoom Out

When you finish using this feature, leave in one of the following ways:

• Select another screen by pressing the appropriate key, such as TRACE or GRAPH.

• Press 2nd [QUIT] to return to the Home screen.

Setting Zoom Factors

Zoom factors determine the extent of the change for the viewing rectangle created by Zoom In or Zoom Out on a graph. Before using Zoom In or Zoom Out, you can review or change the zoom factors.

Zoom Factors

Zoom factors are positive numbers (not necessarily integers) greater than or equal to 1. They define the magnification or reduction factor used to zoom in or out around a point (see pages 3–13 and 3–14).

Checking XFact and YFact

To review the current values of the zoom factors, select ⟨Set Factors⟩ from the ZOOM menu.

The ZOOM FACTORS screen appears (the values shown are the defaults).

```
ZOOM FACTORS
XFact=4
YFact=4
```

Changing XFact and YFact

If they are not what you want, change the zoom factors in one of the following ways:

- Enter a new value. The original value is cleared automatically when you begin typing.

- Position the cursor over the digit you want to change. Then type over it or use DEL to delete it.

The new values are retained in memory.

Leaving ZOOM FACTORS

When the zoom factor values are as you want them, leave ZOOM FACTORS in one of the following ways:

- Select another screen by pressing the appropriate key, such as GRAPH or ZOOM.

- Press 2nd [QUIT] to return to the Home screen.

Using Other ZOOM Features

Four of the ZOOM features reset the RANGE variables to predefined values or use factors to adjust the RANGE variables. Xres remains unchanged, except in Standard.

Square

The TI–81 replots the functions, redefining the viewing rectangle using values based on the current RANGE variables, but adjusted to equalize the width of the dots on the X and Y axes. **Xscl** and **Yscl** remain unchanged. This feature makes the graph of a circle look like a circle (see page 3–20).

The TI–81 replots the graph as soon as the menu selection is made. The midpoint of the current graph (not the axis) becomes the midpoint of the new graph.

Standard

The TI–81 updates the RANGE variables to the standard default values and replots the graph as soon as the menu selection is made. The RANGE variable standard defaults are:

Xmin $= -10$	**Ymin** $= -10$	**Xres** $= 1$
Xmax $= 10$	**Ymax** $= 10$	
Xscl $= 1$	**Yscl** $= 1$	

Trig

The TI–81 updates the RANGE variables using preset values appropriate for trig functions and replots the graph as soon as the menu selection is made. The trig RANGE variable values in Radians mode are:

Xmin $= -2\pi$	**Ymin** $= -3$
Xmax $= 2\pi$	**Ymax** $= 3$
Xscl $= \pi/2$	**Yscl** $= .25$

Note: The display shows the numeric values of 2π, 6.283185307, and $\pi/2$, 1.570796327.

Integer

When you select ‹Integer› from the ZOOM menu, you can move the cursor to the point that you want as the center of the new viewing rectangle and then press ENTER.

The TI–81 replots the functions, redefining the viewing rectangle so that the mid-point of each dot on the X and Y axis is an integer. **Xscl** and **Yscl** are equal to 10.

Using RANGE Variables

For advanced applications, such as programming, values can be stored directly to the RANGE variables using the VARS RNG menu.

Storing to a RANGE Variable

To store a value to a RANGE variable, begin on a blank line on the Home screen or in a program.

1. Enter the value that you want to store. This value can be an expression.

2. Press $\boxed{\text{STO►}}$.

3. Press $\boxed{\text{VARS}}$ $\boxed{◄}$ to display the VARS (Variables) RNG (Range) menu.

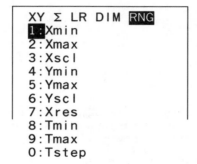

```
XY Σ LR DIM RNG
1:Xmin
2:Xmax
3:Xscl
4:Ymin
5:Ymax
6:Yscl
7:Xres
8:Tmin
9:Tmax
0:Tstep
```

Tmin, **Tmax**, and **Tstep** are described in Chapter 4.

4. Select the RANGE variable to which you want to store. The name of the variable is copied to the current cursor location in the instruction you are editing.

5. Press $\boxed{\text{ENTER}}$ to complete the instruction.

When the instruction is executed, the TI–81 stores the value in the RANGE variable.

Note: You also can recall a RANGE variable into an expression using the VARS RNG menu by performing steps 3 and 4.

Using the Y-VARS Menu

For advanced applications, such as programming or defining one function in terms of others, functions can be stored to or accessed by using the name of the function as a variable using the Y-VARS menu. Functions also can be selected or unselected from a program using the Y-VARS menu.

Using the Name of a Function in the Y= List as a Variable

To use the name of a function in the Y= list as a variable:

1. Press $\boxed{\text{2nd}}$ [Y-VARS] to display the Y-VARS Y menu. Select the function variable name. The name is copied to the current cursor location.

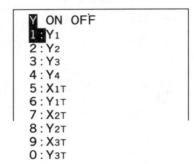

```
Y  ON  OFF
1:Y1
2:Y2
3:Y3
4:Y4
5:X1T
6:Y1T
7:X2T
8:Y2T
9:X3T
0:Y3T
```

2. Continue entering the expression. When the expression is evaluated, the value of the function at the current value of X is used.

Defining Functions

To store an expression as a function in the Y= list, begin on a blank line on the Home screen or in a program.

1. Press $\boxed{\text{ALPHA}}$ ["], enter the expression, and then press $\boxed{\text{ALPHA}}$ ["] again.

2. Press $\boxed{\text{STO}\blacktriangleright}$.

3. Press $\boxed{\text{2nd}}$ [Y-VARS] to display the Y-VARS Y menu. Select the function variable name. The name is copied to the current cursor location.

4. Press $\boxed{\text{ENTER}}$ to complete the instruction. The completed instruction is:

   "expression" →Y*n*

When the instruction is executed, the TI–81 stores the expression to the Y= list, selects the function, and displays the message **Done**.

Turning a Function in the Y= List On or Off

In addition to selecting functions on the Y= edit screen (see page 3–6), you can use the [Y-vars] menu to select or unselect a function in the Y= list. Begin on a blank line on the Home screen or in a program.

1. Press 2nd [Y-vars] to display the Y-VARS menus.

2. Select the appropriate menu.

   • To display the Y-VARS ON menu, press ▶.

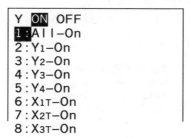

```
Y ON OFF
1:All-On
2:Y1-On
3:Y2-On
4:Y3-On
5:Y4-On
6:X1T-On
7:X2T-On
8:X3T-On
```

   • To display the Y-VARS OFF menu, press ◀.

```
Y ON OFF
1:All-Off
2:Y1-Off
3:Y2-Off
4:Y3-Off
5:Y4-Off
6:X1T-Off
7:X2T-Off
8:X3T-Off
```

3. Select the instruction you want. The instruction is copied to the current cursor location.

4. Press ENTER to complete the instruction. When the instruction is executed, the status of each function in the Y= list is set appropriately and **Done** is displayed.

Example: Graphing a Circle

Graph a circle on the TI-81 and then use the Zoom Square feature to adjust the display to make the functions appear as a circle.

Problem

Graph a circle of radius 10, centered around the origin.

Solution

To graph a circle, you must enter separate formulas for the upper and lower portions of the circle. Use Connected Line mode.

1. Press $\boxed{Y=}$. Enter the expressions to define the functions. The top half of the circle is defined by

   $$Y1 = \sqrt{(100-X^2)}$$

   The bottom half of the circle is defined by

   $$Y2 = -Y1 \quad \text{or} \quad Y2 = -\sqrt{(100-X^2)}$$

2. Press $\boxed{ZOOM}$ and then select ⟨Standard⟩. This is a quick way to reset the RANGE variables to the standard defaults. It also graphs the functions, so you do not need to press $\boxed{GRAPH}$.

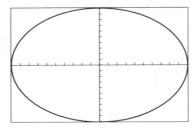

   Notice that the functions appear as an ellipse.

3. To adjust the display so that each "dot" has an equal width and height, press $\boxed{ZOOM}$ and then select ⟨Square⟩. The functions are replotted and now appear as a circle on the display.

4. To see the effect of the Zoom **Square** instruction on the RANGE variables, press $\boxed{RANGE}$ and notice the new values for **Xmin**, **Xmax**, **Ymin**, and **Ymax**.

Chapter 4: Parametric Graphing

This chapter describes how to graph parametric equations on the TI-81. Before doing parametric graphing, you should be familiar with Chapter 3, Function Graphing.

Chapter Contents

Defining and Displaying a Parametric Graph

Parametric equations consist of an X component and a Y component, each expressed in terms of the same independent variable T. Up to three pairs of parametric equations can be defined and graphed at a time.

Steps in Defining a Graph

The steps for defining a parametric graph are the same as those for defining a function graph. Differences are noted below.

Setting Graph Modes

Press MODE to display the MODE settings. The current settings are highlighted. To graph parametric equations, you must select ⟨Param⟩ (see page 3–3) before you enter RANGE variables or enter the components of parametric equations. Also, you usually should select ⟨Connected⟩ to obtain a more meaningful parametric graph.

Displaying the Components of Parametric Equations

Press Y= to display the Y= edit screen.

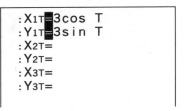

On this screen, you display and enter both X and Y components. There are three pairs of components, each defined in terms of T.

Entering Expressions to Define Components of Parametric Equations

To enter the two expressions that define a new parametric equation, follow the procedure on page 3–4.

• You must define both the X and Y components in a pair.

• The independent variable in each component must be T. You may press the X|T key, rather than pressing ALPHA [T], to enter the parametric variable T. (Parametric mode defines the independent variable as T.)

The procedures for editing, clearing, and leaving are the same as for function graphing (see page 3–5).

Selecting Parametric Equations	Only the parametric equations you select are graphed. You may select up to three equations at a time. Press [Y=] to display the Y= edit screen to select and unselect equations. The = sign on the selected equations is highlighted.

To change the selection status of a parametric equation:

1. Place the cursor over the = sign on either the X or Y component.

2. Press [ENTER] to change the status. The status on both the X and Y components is changed.

Note: When you edit either component or enter both components of an equation, that equation is selected automatically.

Setting the RANGE Variables	Press [RANGE] to display the current RANGE variable values. The values shown below are the standard defaults in Radian mode. Notice that **Xres**, which appeared on the function graphing RANGE edit screen, is not here; but three new variables, **Tmin**, **Tmax**, and **Tstep**, are.

Setting	Meaning
RANGE	
Tmin=0	The smallest T value to be evaluated
Tmax=2π	The largest T value to be evaluated
Tstep=π/30	The increment between T values
Xmin=−10	The smallest X value to be displayed
Xmax=10	The largest X value to be displayed
Xscl=1	The spacing between X tick marks
Ymin=−10	The smallest Y value to be displayed
Ymax=10	The largest Y value to be displayed
Yscl=1	The spacing between Y tick marks

Note: The display shows the numeric value of 2π, 6.283185307, for **Tmax** and .104719755 for **Tstep**.

To change the value of a RANGE variable or to leave the screen, follow the procedures on page 3–7.

Defining and Displaying a Parametric Graph (Continued)

Displaying a Graph

When you press [GRAPH], the TI–81 plots the selected parametric equations. It evaluates both the X and the Y component for each value of T (from **Tmin** to **Tmax** in intervals of **Tstep**) and then plots each point defined by X and Y. The RANGE variables define the viewing rectangle.

As a graph is plotted, the TI–81 updates the variables X, Y, and T.

The "Smart Graph" feature (see page 3–8) also applies to parametric graphs.

Using the RANGE Variables and Y-VARS Menus

For advanced applications, such as programming, you can store values directly to RANGE variables (see page 3–17). You can access functions by using the name of the component of the equation as a variable (see page 3–18). You also can select or unselect parametric equations from a program (see page 3–19).

Exploring a Parametric Graph

As in function graphing, three tools are available for exploring a graph: using the free-moving cursor, tracing an equation, and zooming.

The Free-Moving Cursor

The free-moving cursor (see page 3-9) works in parametric graphing just as it does in function graphing. In Rectangular mode, moving the cursor updates and displays the values of the variables X and Y. (In Polar mode, the variables X, Y, R, and θ are updated, and R and θ are displayed.)

The TRACE Feature

The TRACE feature (see page 3-10) lets you move the cursor along the equation one **Tstep** at a time. When you begin a trace, the blinking cursor is on the first selected equation at the middle T value and the coordinate values of X, Y, and T (or R, θ, and T) are displayed at the bottom of the screen.

In Rectangular mode, tracing updates and displays the values of the variables X, Y, and T. (In Polar mode, the variables X, Y, R, θ, and T are updated, and R, θ, and T are displayed.) The X and Y (or R and θ) values are calculated from T.

If the cursor moves off the top or bottom of the screen, the coordinate values displayed at the bottom of the screen continue to change appropriately.

Panning is not possible on parametric equations. To see a section of the equation not displayed on the graph, you must change the RANGE variables.

The ZOOM Features

The ZOOM features (see pages 3-11 through 3-16) work in parametric graphing as they do in function graphing.

Only the X (**Xmin**, **Xmax**, and **Xscl**) and Y (**Ymin**, **Ymax**, and **Yscl**) RANGE variables are affected. The T RANGE variables (**Tmin**, **Tmax**, and **Tstep**) are not affected, except when you select ⟨Standard⟩: **Tmin** = 0, **Tmax** = 2π, and **Tstep** = $\pi/30$. You may want to change the T RANGE variable values to ensure that sufficient points are plotted.

Example: Simulating Motion

Graph the parametric equation that describes the position over time of a ball that has been kicked.

Problem

Graph the position of a ball kicked at an angle of 60° with an initial velocity of 40 feet per second. (Ignore air resistance.) What is the maximum height and when is it reached? How far away and when does the ball strike the ground?

If v_0 is the initial velocity and θ is the angle, then the horizontal component of the position of the ball as a function of time is described by

$$X(T) = T v_0 \cos \theta$$

The vertical component of the position of the ball as a function of time is described by

$$Y(T) = -16 T^2 + T v_0 \sin \theta$$

Solution

1. Press MODE. Select Parametric, Connected Line, and Degree mode.

2. Press Y=. Enter the expressions to define the parametric equation in terms of T.

   X1T=40Tcos 60
   Y1T=40Tsin 60−16T²

3. Press RANGE. Set the RANGE variables appropriately for this problem.

Tmin = 0	Xmin = −5	Ymin = −5
Tmax = 2.5	Xmax = 50	Ymax = 20
Tstep = .02	Xscl = 5	Yscl = 5

4. Press GRAPH to graph the position of the ball as a function of time.

5. Now press TRACE to explore the graph. When you press TRACE, the values for X, Y, and T are displayed at the bottom of the screen. These values change as you trace the graph.

   Move the cursor along the path of the ball to investigate these values.

Example: Graphing a Polar Equation

Graph the polar equation that defines the Spiral of Archimedes.

Problem

The spiral of Archimedes is the name given to the curve defined by the polar equation $r = a\theta$.

A polar equation $r = f(\theta)$ can be graphed using the parametric graphing features of the TI–81 by applying the conversion formulas, $X = f(\theta) \cos(\theta)$ and $Y = f(\theta) \sin(\theta)$. Thus, the spiral of Archimedes (when $a = .5$) can be expressed parametrically as

$$X = .5\,\theta \cos(\theta)$$
$$Y = .5\,\theta \sin(\theta)$$

Solution

Graph the equation using the standard default viewing rectangle, Radian mode, and Connected Line mode.

1. Press MODE. Select Parametric mode. Choose the defaults for the other modes.

2. Press Y=. Enter the expressions to define the parametric equation in terms of T.

   X1T = .5Tcos T
   Y1T = .5Tsin T

3. Press ZOOM. Select ⟨Standard⟩ to graph the equation in the standard default viewing rectangle.

   The graph shows only the first loop of the spiral. This is because the standard default values for the RANGE variables define **Tmax** as 2π.

4. To explore the behavior of the graph further, press RANGE and change **Tmax** to 25.

5. Press GRAPH to display the new graph.

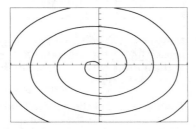

Example: Graphing a Parametric Equation

Graph the parametric equation of an eight-petal "rose".

Problem

A complete graph of the parametric equation

$X(\theta) = 11 \sin 4\theta \cos \theta$
$Y(\theta) = 11 \sin 4\theta \sin \theta$

has two petals in each of the four quadrants.

Solution

Graph this equation using the standard default viewing rectangle, Radian mode, and Connected Line mode.

1. Press MODE. Select Parametric mode. Choose the defaults for the other modes.

2. Press Y=. Enter the expressions to define the parametric equation in terms of T.

   X1T=11sin 4Tcos T
   Y1T=11sin 4Tsin T

3. Press ZOOM. Select ⟨Standard⟩ to graph the equation in the standard default viewing rectangle.

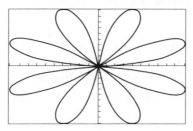

4. Now press TRACE to explore the graph. When you press TRACE, the values for X, Y, and T are displayed at the bottom of the screen. These values change as you trace the graph.

   Tracing begins at the middle T value. As you press ▶ to trace the curve, the cursor moves around four of the petals until it reaches **Tmax**. To trace the other petals, press ◀ until you reach **Tmin**.

Chapter 5: The DRAW Features

This chapter describes how to use the DRAW features of the TI-81 to draw lines, points, functions, and shaded areas on a graph. Before using the DRAW features, you should be familiar with Chapter 3, Function Graphing.

Chapter Contents

The DRAW Menu

Pressing [2nd] [DRAW] accesses instructions that draw lines,
points, functions, and shaded areas on a graph. You can draw
lines and points directly on a graph using the cursor to
identify coordinates. You also can use these instructions
from the Home screen or a program.

The DRAW Menu

Menu	Meaning
DRAW	
1:ClrDraw	Clears drawings
2:Line(	Draws a straight line
3:PT-On(	Turns on a point
4:PT-Off(	Turns off a point
5:PT-Chg(	Reverses a point
6:DrawF	Draws a function
7:Shade(	Shades part of the graph

Notes about the DRAW Menu

The current menu name and item number are
highlighted.

Each of the DRAW instructions can be entered on a blank
line on the Home screen or program edit screen. When
you select an instruction from the DRAW menu, the
name of the instruction is copied to the current cursor
location. You then enter the argument or arguments.

You can also use the line and point DRAW instructions
and the cursor to draw directly on a graph. Display a
graph, press [2nd] [DRAW], and select an instruction from
the DRAW menu. Then use the cursor and [ENTER] to
define the drawing.

The DRAW instructions can be used on both function
graphs and parametric graphs. The coordinates for
DRAW instructions are the x- and y-coordinate values of
the display.

General Notes about the DRAW Instructions

Any drawings remain on the graph until a change prompts the "Smart Graph" feature (see page 3–8) to replot the graph.

The DRAW Instructions

The DRAW instructions let you draw on the current graph. When the "Smart Graph" feature replots a graph, all points, lines, functions drawn by the **DrawF** instruction, and shading are erased.

RANGE variables are not updated by DRAW instructions.

Before Drawing on a Graph

Because the DRAW instructions also display the graph of the currently selected functions, the following steps may be appropriate before drawing on a graph.

1. Set the modes appropriate to the graph (see page 3–3).

2. Enter or edit an expression to define a function in the Y= list (see pages 3–4 through 3–5).

3. Select or unselect the functions in the Y= list (see page 3–6).

4. Define the viewing rectangle appropriate to the graph (see page 3–7).

Leaving DRAW

To leave the DRAW menu without making a selection, do one of the following:

• Select another screen by pressing the appropriate key, such as Y= or GRAPH.

• Press 2nd [QUIT] to return to the Home screen.

Clearing Drawings on a Graph

The ClrDraw instruction clears all lines, points, functions drawn by the DrawF instruction, and shading currently drawn on a graph.

Clearing Drawings

To clear drawings on a graph, begin on a blank line on the Home screen or program edit screen.

1. Press 2nd [DRAW]. Select ⟨ClrDraw⟩ from the DRAW menu. The instruction **ClrDraw** is copied to the current cursor location.

2. Press ENTER to complete the instruction.

   The completed instruction is:

   ClrDraw

When the instruction is executed, all drawn lines, points, functions drawn by the **DrawF** instruction, and shaded areas are erased and the message **Done** is displayed. The next time that you display the graph, all drawings will be gone.

Drawing a Line

While a graph is displayed, the DRAW Line instruction lets
you define a line on the graph using the cursor. You also can
draw a line on a graph from the Home screen or from a
program.

**Using the Line
Instruction from
a Graph**

To draw a line while a graph is displayed:

1. Press [2nd] [DRAW]. Select ‹Line(› from the DRAW
   menu.

2. Position the cursor at the beginning point of the line
   you want to draw, and then press [ENTER].

3. Move the cursor to the end point of the line you want
   to draw. The line is displayed as you move the cursor.
   Press [ENTER] and the line is drawn on the graph
   between the two selected points.

You can continue to draw lines by repeating steps 2 and
3. Press [GRAPH] to leave DRAW **Line.**

**Using the Line
Instruction from
the Home Screen
or a Program**

To draw a line using an instruction, begin on a blank line
on the Home screen or program edit screen.

1. Press [2nd] [DRAW]. Select ‹Line(› from the DRAW
   menu. The instruction **Line(** is copied to the current
   cursor location.

2. Enter the values for the four arguments, separated by
   commas:

   • The X value of the beginning coordinate

   • The Y value of the beginning coordinate

   • The X value of the ending coordinate

   • The Y value of the ending coordinate

3. Press [)].

4. Press [ENTER] to complete the instruction.

   The completed instruction is:

   Line(*Xbeg*,*Ybeg*,*Xend*,*Yend*)

When the instruction is executed, the line is drawn on a
graph of currently selected functions in the Y= list.

Drawing a Point

While a graph is displayed, the DRAW PT instructions let you turn on, turn off, or reverse a point on the graph using the cursor. The same activities can be done from the Home screen or from a program.

Using the PT-On Instruction from a Graph

To turn on a point while a graph is displayed:

1. Press [2nd] [DRAW]. Select ⟨PT-On(⟩ from the DRAW menu.

2. Position the cursor at the location on the screen where you want to draw the point and then press [ENTER].

   The point is drawn.

   You can continue to draw points by repeating step 2. Press [GRAPH] to leave DRAW **PT**.

Using the PT-On Instruction from the Home Screen or a Program

To turn on a point using an instruction, begin on a blank line on the Home screen or program edit screen.

1. Press [2nd] [DRAW]. Select ⟨PT-On(⟩ from the DRAW menu. The instruction **PT-On(** is copied to the current cursor location.

2. Enter the values for the arguments, separated by a comma:

   • The X value of the coordinate

   • The Y value of the coordinate

3. Press [)].

4. Press [ENTER] to complete the instruction.

   The completed instruction is:

   PT-On(X, Y)

   When the instruction is executed, the point is drawn on a graph of currently selected functions in the Y= list.

Using the PT-Off and PT-Chg Instructions

The procedure for using **PT-Off** to turn off (erase) a point is the same as for **PT-On**.

The procedure for using **PT-Chg** to change (reverse) the status of a point is the same as for **PT-On**.

Drawing a Function

The DrawF instruction draws a function on a graph. The function drawn by the DrawF instruction is temporary; it is not saved as a function in the Y= list.

Using the DrawF Instruction

The **DrawF** instruction draws a function of X. It uses the current RANGE variables. To draw a function, begin on a blank line on the Home screen or program edit screen.

1. Press RANGE to check and modify the RANGE variables, if desired (see page 3-7).

2. Press 2nd [DRAW]. Select ⟨DrawF⟩ from the DRAW menu. The instruction **DrawF** is copied to the current cursor location.

3. Enter the argument as an expression in terms of X.

4. Press ENTER to complete the instruction.

   The completed instruction is:

   DrawF *function*

   When the instruction is executed, the function is drawn on a graph of currently selected functions in the Y= list and the variables X and Y are updated.

   Note: Because a function drawn with the **DrawF** instruction is temporary, it cannot be traced.

Shading an Area on a Graph

The DRAW Shade instruction shades the area on a graph that is below one specified function and above another. It also draws the two functions.

The Shading Parameters

The **Shade(** instruction can have five arguments. The first two arguments are required. Only the areas where the first argument is less than the second argument are shaded. The last three arguments are optional.

The first argument defines the lower boundary of the shaded area and the function to be drawn. The argument can be:

- An expression in terms of X. For example, **X^2+1** shades the area above the curve X^2+1.

- A value or a variable. For example, **3** shades the area above the line Y=3.

- An expression stored in a function in the Y= list and accessed from the Y-VARS Y menu. For example, if **Y2 = X^2+5**, then **Y2** shades the area above the curve X^2+5.

The second argument defines the upper boundary of the shaded area and the function to be drawn. The argument can be any of the types described for the first argument.

The third argument defines the resolution (degree of shading). Resolution is an integer from 1 to 8. If the argument is not specified, the default is the current value of **Xres**.

The fourth argument defines the left boundary of the shaded area (the beginning X). It can be a value, a variable, or an expression. If the argument is not specified, the default is the current value of **Xmin**.

The fifth argument defines the right boundary of the shaded area (the ending X). It can be a value, a variable, or an expression. If the argument is not specified, the default is the current value of **Xmax**.

Shading a Drawing

To shade an area on a graph, begin on a blank line on the Home screen or program edit screen.

1. Press [2nd] [DRAW]. Select ⟨Shade(⟩ from the DRAW menu. The instruction **Shade(** is copied to the current cursor location.

2. Enter the first argument and then press [ALPHA] [,].

3. Enter the second argument.

   • If you do not want to enter the last three arguments, go to step 5.

   • If you want to enter any of the last three arguments, press [ALPHA] [,] and then go to step 4.

4. Enter the optional arguments, separated by commas.

   Note: You can use the VARS menu (see page 3-17) to select **Xres**, **Xmin**, or **Xmax** for any of these arguments.

5. Press [ )].

6. Press [ENTER] to complete the instruction.

   The completed instruction is:

   Shade(*lowerfunc*,*upperfunc*,*resolution*,*Xbeg*,*Xend*)

   When the instruction is executed, the shaded area and the two functions, as defined by the arguments, are drawn on a graph of currently selected functions in the Y= list and the variables X and Y are updated.

Example: Shading the Area between Two Functions

Shade an area on a graph above one function and below another.

Problem

Shade the area on the graph that is above the function Y=X+1 and below the function Y=X³−8X.

Solution

1. Press $\boxed{\text{Y=}}$ to see that all functions are unselected.

   Use the standard default viewing rectangle. Press $\boxed{\text{RANGE}}$ to check and change the viewing rectangle, or $\boxed{\text{ZOOM}}$ ⟨Standard⟩ to reset the RANGE variables.

2. Press $\boxed{\text{2nd}}$ [QUIT] to return to the Home screen. Begin on a blank line.

3. Press $\boxed{\text{2nd}}$ [DRAW]. Select ⟨Shade(⟩ to copy the **Shade(** instruction to the Home screen.

4. Enter the lower function, X+1, followed by a comma, and then enter the upper function, X³−8X. Because you are not going to set left or right boundaries or change the resolution, enter a close parentheses. The completed instruction is:

   Shade(X+1,X³−8X)

5. Press $\boxed{\text{ENTER}}$.

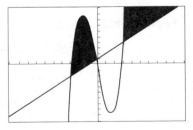

Chapter 6: Using Matrices

This chapter describes the matrix features of the TI-81. The TI-81 can store up to three matrices. The maximum dimension of each matrix is six rows by six columns.

Chapter Contents

The MATRX (Matrix) Menus

Pressing MATRX accesses the matrix operations. They are grouped functionally in two menus: MATRIX (functions) and EDIT (defining a matrix).

The MATRX Menus

Menu	Meaning
MATRIX EDIT	
1 : RowSwap (	Swaps two rows of a matrix
2 : Row+ (	Adds two rows, stores in second row
3 : *Row (	Multiplies row by a scalar value
4 : *Row+ (	Multiplies row, adds to second row
5 : det	Calculates the determinant
6 : T	Transposes the matrix
MATRIX **EDIT**	
1 : [A] 6×6	Edits matrix A
2 : [B] 6×6	Edits matrix B
3 : [C] 6×6	Edits matrix C

Notes about the MATRX Menus

The current menu name and item number are highlighted.

When you select a function from the MATRIX menu, the name of the function is copied to the current cursor location in the expression you are editing.

When you select a matrix from the EDIT menu, the MATRX edit screen appears. Note that 6×6 is the largest dimension available for a matrix.

Defining a Matrix

To define a matrix, select one of the three matrices, [A], [B], or [C], and define the dimensions of that matrix. On the top line of the MATRX edit screen, a small graphic box indicates the size of the matrix and the element where the cursor is located.

Selecting a Matrix

To define a matrix, you first must select the matrix you want to define.

1. Press MATRX ▶ to select the MATRX EDIT menu.

2. Press the number of the matrix you want to create (either [A], [B], or [C]). The MATRX edit screen appears.

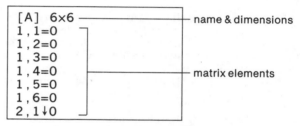

The blinking cursor is on the row dimension. A ↓ is displayed in place of the = on the last line if there are more than seven elements in the matrix.

Accepting or Changing Matrix Dimensions

The dimensions of the matrix (row × column) are displayed on the top line. You must accept or change the dimensions each time you enter or edit a matrix.

1. Accept or change the number of rows.

   • To accept the number, press ENTER.

   • To change the number, enter the number of rows (up to six), and then press ENTER.

   The cursor moves to the number of columns.

2. Accept or change the number of columns.

   • To accept the number, press ENTER.

   • To change the number, enter the number of columns (up to six), and then press ENTER.

   The cursor moves to the first matrix element (1,1).

Entering and Editing Matrix Elements

After the dimensions of the matrix are set, values can be entered into the matrix elements on the MATRX edit screen. On the top line of the screen, a small graphic box indicates the size of the matrix and the element where the cursor is located.

Entering Matrix Elements

To enter values in a matrix:

1. Enter the value you want and then press ENTER . The cursor moves to the next element.

2. Continue entering values.

Editing a Matrix

To edit a matrix:

1. If the MATRX edit screen is not currently displayed, press MATRX ► to display the MATRX EDIT menu, and then press the number of the matrix you want to edit. The MATRX edit screen appears.

2. Use ▼ to move the cursor to the matrix element you want to change.

3. Enter the new value using one of these methods:

   • Enter a new value. The original value is cleared automatically when you begin typing.

   • Use ► or ◄ to position the cursor over the digit you want to change. Then type over it or use DEL to delete it.

4. When you have changed the matrix element value, press ENTER . The cursor moves to the next value.

Leaving the MATRX Edit Screen

When you finish entering and editing matrix values:

   • Select another screen by pressing the appropriate key, such as MATRX .

   • Press 2nd [QUIT] to return to the Home screen.

Clearing a Matrix

To clear all the elements of a matrix, store 0 to that matrix. For example, press 0 STO► 2nd [lAl] to set all the elements in matrix [A] to zero.

Notes about Using Matrices

Matrices can be displayed, copied, and used in the same way as a variable.

Displaying a Stored Matrix

You can display a stored matrix in one of two ways:

- On the Home screen, press 2nd [[A]], for example, and then press ENTER. The matrix is displayed in matrix format:

```
[A]
[ 1  0  1  0]
[ 1  2  0  0]
[ 3  1  1  1]
```

If all of the matrix does not fit in the display, as indicated by dots on the right of the screen, use ▶ and ◀ to display the rest of the matrix.

- Press MATRX ▶ to select the MATRX EDIT menu, and then press the number of the matrix you want. The MATRX edit screen appears (see page 6–3). Use ▼ to view the elements.

Copying One Matrix to Another

Copy one matrix to another by storing the matrix to another matrix location. For example, press 2nd [[A]] STO▶ 2nd [[B]] to copy [A] to [B]. The dimensions of [B] will be the dimensions of [A].

Using a Matrix in an Expression

To enter the name of a matrix into an expression, press 2nd [[A]], 2nd [[B]], or 2nd [[C]]. The name of the matrix is copied to the current cursor location in the expression you are editing.

Results of Matrix Calculations

If the result of evaluating an expression is a matrix, it is stored in the variable **Ans**. To save the resulting matrix, store **Ans** to a matrix. For example, press 2nd [ANS] STO▶ 2nd [[A]] to store the resulting matrix to matrix [A].

Matrix Math Functions

A matrix can be used in most operations where a variable can be used. However, the dimensions of the matrices must be appropriate for the operation.

Operations	Example Keystrokes	Display
Addition	[2nd] [[A]] [+] [2nd] [[B]]	[A]+[B]
Subtraction	[2nd] [[B]] [−] [2nd] [[C]]	[B]−[C]
Multiplication	[2nd] [[A]]] [2nd] [[C]]	[A][C]
Scalar multiplication	3 [2nd] [[A]]	3[A]
Inversion	[2nd] [[C]] [x⁻¹]	[C]⁻¹
Squaring	[2nd] [[B]] [x²]	[B]²
Determinant	[MATRX] ⟨det⟩ [2nd] [[A]]	det [A]
Transposition	[2nd] [[B]] [MATRX] ⟨T⟩	[B]ᵀ
Round	[MATH] [▶] ⟨Round(⟩ [2nd] [[A]] [ALPHA] [,] 0 [)]	Round(Round([A] Round([A],0)
Negation	[(−)] [2nd] [[C]]	−[C]

Notes about Matrix Math Operations

The TI–81 has one temporary matrix available for intermediate results. Therefore, an expression cannot result in more than one intermediate matrix during evaluation.

As an example, evaluating $[A]^{-1}*[B]^{-1}$ would require two intermediate (temporary) matrices, one for each inverse. To use the TI–81 to evaluate this expression, break the expression into two expressions: first calculate $[A]^{-1}$ (the result is stored in **Ans**), and then multiply **Ans** by $[B]^{-1}$.

Operation	Restrictions/Results
Addition	The dimensions of the matrices must be the same. The result is a matrix of the same dimensions in which the elements are the sum of [A] and [B] elements.
Subtraction	The dimensions of the matrices must be the same. The result is a matrix of the same dimensions in which the elements are the difference of [B] and [C] elements.
Multiplication	The column dimension of [A] must match the row dimension of [C].
Scalar multiplication	There are no restrictions. The result is a matrix whose elements are the elements of [A] multiplied by the scalar.
Inversion	The row dimension and the column dimension of the matrix must be equal. The determinant cannot equal zero.
Squaring	The row dimension and the column dimension of the matrix must be equal.
Determinant	The row dimension and the column dimension of the matrix must be equal. The result is a scalar.
Transposition	There are no restrictions. The result is a matrix in which element(row,col) is swapped with element(col,row).
Round	There are no restrictions. The result is a matrix in which every element is rounded as defined by the second argument.
Negation	There are no restrictions. The result is a matrix in which the sign of every element is changed (reversed).

Using the Row Operations

Four row operations are accessed from the MATRIX menu.
These functions, which can be used in an expression, do not
change the original matrix. The result of each of these
functions is a temporary matrix.

The RowSwap Function

The **RowSwap** function swaps two rows in a matrix.

This function requires three arguments: the matrix
name, the number of the first row you want to swap, and
the number of the row you want to swap with it. All
arguments must be separated by commas.

The completed function is:

RowSwap(*matrix,row1,row2*)

Swapping Rows in a Matrix

Swap rows 2 and 3 in matrix [A]. Assume [A] contains:

```
[ 5  3  1]
[ 2  0  4]
[ 3  1  2]
```

Procedure	Keystrokes	Display
Select ‹RowSwap(›	[MATRX]	
	‹RowSwap(›	RowSwap (
Enter matrix name followed by a comma	[2nd] [[A]] [ALPHA] [,]	RowSwap ([A] ,
Enter 1st row to swap	2 [ALPHA] [,]	RowSwap ([A] , 2 ,
Enter 2nd row to swap	3 [)]	RowSwap ([A] , 2 , 3)
Evaluate expression	[ENTER]	RowSwap ([A] , 2 , 3)
		[5 3 1]
		[3 1 2]
		[2 0 4]

The procedure for entering other row functions is
similar. Row numbers and scalar values can be
expressions, which are evaluated when you press [ENTER]
or when the program is executed.

Using the Row+ Function

The **Row+** function adds two rows and stores the results in the second row.

This function requires three arguments: the matrix name, the number of the row to be added, and the number of the row to be added to and in which to store the results. Separate the arguments by commas.

The completed function is:

Row+(*matrix*,*row1*,*row2*)

Using the *Row Function

The *****Row** function multiplies a row by a scalar value and stores the results in the same row.

This function requires three arguments: the scalar value (which can be an expression), the matrix name, and the number of the row to be multiplied. Separate the arguments by commas.

The completed function is:

*Row(*scalar*,*matrix*,*row*)

Using the *Row+ Function

The *****Row+** function multiplies a row by a scalar value, adds the results to a second row, and stores the results in the second row.

This function requires four arguments: the scalar value (which can be an expression), the matrix name, the number of the row to be multiplied, and the number of the row to be added to and in which to store the results. Separate the arguments by commas.

The completed function is:

*Row+(*scalar*,*matrix*,*row1*,*row2*)

Storing and Recalling a Matrix Element

A value can be stored directly to or recalled from a specific matrix element on the Home screen or from a program. The element must be within the currently defined matrix dimensions.

Storing to a Matrix Element

To store to a matrix element, begin on a blank line.

1. Enter the value you want to store. This value can be an expression.

2. Press [STO▶].

3. Press [2nd] and then [[A]], [[B]] or [[C]].

4. Press [(], enter the row of the matrix element, and then press [ALPHA] [,].

5. Enter the column of the matrix element, and then press [)].

6. Press [ENTER] to complete the instruction. The completed instruction is:

   value→*matrix*(*row*,*column*)

   When the instruction is executed, the TI-81 stores the value to the element.

   Note: value→matrix stores the value to every element in the matrix.

Using a Matrix Element in an Expression

To use a matrix element as a variable in an expression:

1. Press [2nd] and then [[A]], [[B]] or [[C]] (or [ANS] if it contains a matrix).

2. Press [(], enter the row of matrix element, and then press [ALPHA] [,].

3. Enter the column of the matrix element, and then press [)].

When the expression is evaluated, the value in the matrix element is used.

Storing and Recalling a Matrix Dimension

For advanced applications, such as programming, values can be stored directly to matrix dimension variables. Matrix dimension variables also can be used in expressions.

Storing to a Matrix Dimension Variable

To store a value to a matrix dimension variable, begin on a blank line.

1. Enter the value you want to store. This value can be an expression.

2. Press [STO▶].

3. Press [VARS] [▶] [▶] [▶] to display the VARS DIM menu:

Menu	Meaning
XY Σ LR **DIM** RNG	
1:Arow	Number of rows in matrix [A]
2:Acol	Number of columns in matrix [A]
3:Brow	Number of rows in matrix [B]
4:Bcol	Number of columns in matrix [B]
5:Crow	Number of rows in matrix [C]
6:Ccol	Number of columns in matrix [C]
7:Dim{x}	Length of statistical data list*

* See pages 7–10 and 7–11.

4. Press the number of the matrix dimension variable you want. The name of the variable is copied to the current cursor location.

5. Press [ENTER] to complete the instruction.

When the instruction is executed, the TI–81 stores the value to the matrix dimension variable.

Using a Matrix Dimension Variable in an Expression

To use a matrix dimension in an expression:

1. Press [VARS] [▶] [▶] [▶] to display the VARS DIM menu.

2. Press the number of the matrix dimension variable you want. The name of the variable is copied to the current cursor location in the expression you are editing.

When the expression is evaluated, the value in the matrix dimension is used.

Example: Reducing a Matrix

Use the row operations on the TI–81 to solve a system of two linear equations with three variables.

Problem

You can solve a system of linear equations by expressing the coefficients as elements in a matrix and using row operations to obtain the reduced row echelon form.

Find the solution of

$$x + 2y + 3z = 3$$
$$2x + 3y + 4z = 3$$

Solution

1. Press MATRX. Then select the EDIT screen and enter the following elements into a 2 by 4 matrix, [A].

   [1 2 3 3]
   [2 3 4 3]

2. Press 2nd [QUIT] to return to the Home screen. Begin on a blank line. Press MATRX. Use the *Row+(instruction to multiply row 1 by -2 and add it to row 2. The resulting matrix is displayed and stored in **Ans**. The completed instruction is:

   *Row+(−2,[A],1,2)

3. Press MATRX. Use the *Row(instruction to multiply row 2 of the matrix in **Ans** by -1. The resulting matrix is displayed and stored in **Ans**. The completed instruction is:

   *Row(−1,Ans,2)

4. Press MATRX. Use the *Row+(instruction to multiply row 2 of the matrix in **Ans** by -2 and add it to row 1. The resulting reduced row echelon form of the matrix is displayed and stored in **Ans**. The completed instruction is:

   *Row+(−2,Ans,2,1)

   Resulting in:

   [1 0 −1 −3]   so $x = -3 + z$
   [0 1   2   3] $y = 3 - 2z$

Chapter 7: Performing Statistical Calculations

This chapter describes the tools the TI–81 provides to help enter and analyze statistical data. These include calculating one-variable and two-variable statistical results, performing regression analysis, and displaying the data graphically.

Chapter Contents

The STAT (Statistical) Menus

Pressing [2nd] [STAT] accesses the statistical menus. The statistical operations are grouped functionally into three menus: calculating statistical results, drawing (plotting) the data, and entering or editing the data.

The STAT Menus

Menu	Meaning
CALC DRAW DATA	
1:1-Var	Calculates one-variable results
2:LinReg	Calculates linear regression model
3:LnReg	Calculates logarithmic regression model
4:ExpReg	Calculates exponential regression model
5:PwrReg	Calculates power regression model
CALC **DRAW** DATA	
1:Hist	Draws a histogram
2:Scatter	Draws a scatter plot of the data points
3:xyLine	Plots and connects data points with a line
CALC DRAW **DATA**	
1:Edit	Enters or edits data values
2:ClrStat	Clears data values
3:xSort	Orders data points by X values
4:ySort	Orders data points by Y values

Notes about the STAT Menus

The current menu name and item number are highlighted.

When you select an instruction (except ⟨Edit⟩) from any of the STAT menus, the name of that instruction is copied to the current cursor location.

When you select ⟨Edit⟩ from the STAT DATA menu, the DATA edit screen appears.

Note: The memory used to store statistical data is shared with programs. If there are no stored programs, you can store 150 data points. If you run out of memory, you can free additional memory by erasing a program (see page 8-8). The memory status is displayed on the RESET screen (see page 1-28).

Setting Up a Statistical Analysis

To set up a statistical analysis, clear the data area and then enter the data. Each data point has an X value and a Y value.

Statistical Data

Data points are interpreted as one-variable or two-variable data when you perform an analysis, not when you enter the points.

- In one-variable data, Y values are the frequency of occurrence of the associated X value.

- In two-variable data, the X values are independent variables; the Y values are dependent variables.

Clearing Previous Data

To clear statistical data quickly, begin on a blank line on the Home screen or program edit screen.

1. Press [2nd] [STAT] [◄] to display the STAT DATA menu.

2. Select ⟨ClrStat⟩ from the STAT DATA menu.

   The instruction **ClrStat** is copied to the current cursor location.

3. Press [ENTER] to complete the instruction.

When the instruction is executed, it clears all statistical information stored in memory and the message **Done** is displayed. **ClrStat** clears (blanks) X values and sets the Y values to 1. In addition, it clears the statistical results variables (see page 7–10).

Clearing statistical data does not affect other information in memory, such as nonstatistical variables, matrix values, or programs.

Entering and Editing Data

Data for statistical analysis is entered on the DATA edit screen. The edit screen is a selection on the STAT DATA menu.

Entering a New Set of Data

After you have cleared the old statistical data:

1. Press 2nd [STAT] ◄ to display the STAT DATA menu.

2. Select ⟨Edit⟩. The DATA edit screen appears.

```
DATA
x1=
y1=1
```

The cursor is on the first X value.

3. Enter the value for X and then press ENTER. The cursor moves to the Y value.

4. Enter the value for Y and then press ENTER. The cursor moves to the next X value.

Note: In one-variable data, the Y value represents the frequency of occurrence of the X value and, therefore, must be an integer greater than or equal to zero. Press ENTER to accept the default value of 1; otherwise, type over it to enter the frequency of the X value.

5. Continue entering values.

Leaving the DATA Edit Screen

When you finish entering and editing statistical data values, leave the DATA edit screen in one of the following ways:

• Select another screen by pressing the appropriate key, such as 2nd [STAT].

• Press 2nd [QUIT] to return to the Home screen.

Editing Statistical Data

To edit statistical data, select ⟨Edit⟩ from the STAT DATA menu. The DATA edit screen displays the data you have entered. To change a statistical data value:

1. Move the cursor to the data point you want to change. To move quickly from the first data point to the empty data point after the last data point in the list, press ▲.

2. Enter the new value using one of these methods:

   • Enter a new value. The original value is cleared automatically when you begin typing.

   • Use ▶ or ◀ to position the cursor over the digit you want to change. Then type over it or use DEL to delete it.

3. Press ENTER. The cursor moves to the next value.

Inserting Statistical Data

To insert a new statistical data point:

1. Move the cursor to the data point before which you want to insert.

2. Use ◀ to move the cursor over the = sign of either the X or Y data value.

3. Press INS and a new data point is created. The cursor is on the X value.

4. Enter the values for X and Y.

Deleting Statistical Data

To delete a statistical data point:

1. Move the cursor to the data point you want to delete.

2. Use ◀ to move the cursor over the = sign in either the X value and the Y value.

3. Press DEL and the data point is deleted.

Sorting Data

The TI-81 can sort the current data set into numerical order, from smallest to largest, based on either the X values or the Y values.

Sorting Statistical Data

To sort statistical data, begin on a blank line on the Home screen or program edit screen.

1. Press [2nd] [STAT] [◄] to display the STAT DATA menu.

2. Choose the type of sort you want:

   • To select ⟨xSort⟩, press [3].

   • To select ⟨ySort⟩, press [4].

   The instruction **xSort** or **ySort** is copied to the current cursor location.

3. Press [ENTER] to complete the instruction.

When the instruction is executed, the data points in the list are sorted and the message **Done** is displayed.

Reviewing Sorted Data

You can review sorted data in one of the following ways:

   • To review each data point, press [2nd] [STAT] [◄]. Select ⟨Edit⟩ from the STAT DATA menu.

   • To plot the data, select ⟨xyLine⟩ from the STAT DRAW menu (see pages 7–14 and 7–15).

Calculating One-Variable Statistics

Statistical results are calculated and displayed using the
STAT CALC menu. The 1-Var menu item interprets the X value
as the data and the Y value as the frequency.

Calculating the Results

To calculate one-variable statistical results after entering
the data values, begin on a blank line on the Home screen
or program screen.

1. Press [2nd] [STAT] to display the STAT CALC menu.

2. Select ⟨1-Var⟩.

   The instruction 1-Var is copied to the current cursor
   location.

3. Press [ENTER] to complete the instruction.

When the instruction is executed, the standard
statistical results, $\bar{x}$, Σx, Σx^2, Sx, σx, and n, are calculated
and displayed, as in the sample shown here:

```
1-Var
x̄=2.5
Σx=10
Σx²=30
Sx=1.290994449
σx=1.118033989
n=4
```

In addition, the TI–81 stores the results of the
computations in variables that you can access from the
VARS menu (see page 7–10).

Calculating Two-Variable Statistics

For two-variable data, the STAT CALC menu has four regression models for curve fitting and forecasting. The X value is interpreted as the independent variable and the Y value as the dependent variable. A regression analysis also calculates the standard statistical results.

Calculating the Results

To calculate a regression after entering data, begin on a blank line on the Home screen or program edit screen.

1. Press [2nd] [STAT] to display the STAT CALC menu.

2. Choose the type of regression model you want:

   - To calculate a linear regression model, select ⟨LinReg⟩.

   - To calculate a logarithmic regression model, select ⟨LnReg⟩.

   - To calculate an exponential regression model, select ⟨ExpReg⟩.

   - To calculate a power regression model, select ⟨PwrReg⟩.

   The instruction is copied to the current cursor location.

3. Press [ENTER] to complete the instruction.

When the instruction is executed, the screen displays the most commonly referenced results, as in the sample shown here:

```
LinReg
  a=3
  b=-.5
  r=-.85
```

In addition, the TI-81 stores all the results of the computations in variables, including some not displayed on this screen. See page 7-10 for information about accessing statistical results variables.

The Regression Models

Model	Formula	Restrictions
Linear	$Y = a + bX$	
Logarithmic	$Y = a + b\ln(X)$	All X values > zero
Exponential	$Y = ab^X$	All Y values > zero
Power	$Y = aX^b$	All X and Y > zero

The statistical results are calculated using transformed values:

- The linear model uses X and Y.

- The logarithmic model uses $\ln(X)$ and Y.

- The exponential model uses X and $\ln(Y)$.

- The power model uses $\ln(X)$ and $\ln(Y)$.

The TI-81 calculates the values for **a** and **b** according to the selected regression model. The results are stored in the variables **a** and **b** that you access from the VARS LR menu.

In addition, the TI-81 calculates **r**, the correlation coefficient, which measures the goodness of fit of the equation with the data. In general, the closer **r** is to 1 or -1, the better the fit; the closer **r** is to zero, the worse the fit. You can access **r** from the VARS LR menu.

The TI-81 calculates and stores the regression equation with numeric coefficients in the variable **Reg EQ** (see page 7-13).

The TI-81 also determines other statistical results that are not displayed, but that you can access from other VARS menus (see page 7-10).

Statistical Results Variables

All the statistical results variables, including the regression equation, can be recalled using the VARS menu. The values of the variables can be displayed or included in expressions. These variables are updated when statistical results are calculated; you cannot store to these variables.

The VARS Menu

Menu	Meaning
XY Σ LR DIM RNG	
1: n	Number of data points
2 : $\bar{x}$	Mean of X values
3 : Sx	Sample standard deviation of X
4 : σx	Population standard deviation of X
5 : $\bar{y}$	Mean of Y values
6 : Sy	Sample standard deviation of Y
7 : σy	Population standard deviation of Y
XY **Σ** LR DIM RNG	
1: Σx	Sum of X values
2 : Σx^2	Sum of the squares of X values
3 : Σy	Sum of Y values
4 : Σy^2	Sum of the squares of Y values
5 : Σxy	Sum of the product of X and Y values
XY Σ **LR** DIM RNG	
1: a	Coefficient of regression equation
2 : b	Coefficient of regression equation
3 : r	Correlation coefficient
4 : RegEQ	Regression equation
XY Σ LR **DIM** RNG *	
1: Arow	Number of rows in matrix [A]
2 : Acol	Number of columns in matrix [A]
3 : Brow	Number of rows in matrix [B]
4 : Bcol	Number of columns in matrix [B]
5 : Crow	Number of rows in matrix [C]
6 : Ccol	Number of columns in matrix [C]
7 : Dim{x}	Length of statistical data list

* The VARS RNG menu is described in Chapter 3. The matrix dimensions on the VARS DIM menu are described in Chapter 6.

Notes about the VARS Menus

The current menu name and item number are highlighted.

When you select a variable (except **RegEQ)** from any of the VARS menus, the name of that variable is copied to the current cursor location.

When you select ⟨RegEQ⟩ from the VARS menu, the regression equation with numeric coefficients is copied to the current cursor location.

One-Variable Results

When the **1-Var** instruction from the STAT CALC menu is executed, only the variables $\bar{x}$, Σx, Σx^2, **Sx**, σx, and **n** have a calculated value and are valid in an expression.

Two-Variable Results

When a two-variable regression model from the STAT CALC menu is executed, all the statistical results variables are calculated and are valid in an expression.

The DIM{x} Variable

The TI–81 stores the physical length of the current statistical data list in **DIM**{x}. For two-variable data, **DIM**{x} is equal to **n** (the number of data points). For one-variable data, **DIM**{x} may be different from **n**.

Statistical Results Variables (Continued)

Displaying a Statistical Results Variable

To recall and display the value from a statistical results variable, begin on a blank line on the Home screen.

1. Press VARS to access the VARS menus.

2. Press ▶ as necessary to access the correct menu. Then press the number of the variable you want.

   The variable name is copied to the current cursor location.

3. Press ENTER to display the value of the variable.

Using a Statistical Results Variable in an Expression

To use a statistical results variable in an expression:

1. Press VARS to access the VARS menus.

2. Press ▶ as necessary to access the correct menu. Then press the number of the variable you want.

   The variable name is copied to the current cursor location.

3. Continue entering the expression.

Using RegEQ   The **RegEQ** variable contains the current regression
equation. You can, for example, copy it either to a
function in the Y= list or to the Home screen. To access
RegEQ:

1. Press VARS ▶ ▶ to display the VARS LR menu.

2. Select ⟨RegEQ⟩.

   The expression in **RegEQ** is copied to the current
   cursor location. It contains the numeric values for **a**
   and **b**, not the variable names; for example, 3 + 5X.

3. Press ENTER to complete the expression. When the
   expression is evaluated, the current value of X is used.

Drawing Statistical Data

After the statistical data is entered, an operation from the
STAT DRAW menu can be selected to display statistical data
graphically. See Chapters 3 and 5 for information about
graphing and drawing.

**Before Plotting
the Data**

The STAT DRAW operations are tied closely to the
GRAPH and DRAW operations.

- The RANGE variables define the viewing rectangle.

- Statistical data is plotted on the graph of currently
  selected functions in the Y= list.

Before plotting statistical data:

1. Press $\boxed{\text{RANGE}}$ to check and change the RANGE
   variables (see page 3–7).

2. Press $\boxed{\text{Y=}}$ to edit, select, or unselect functions in the
   Y= list (see pages 3–4 through 3–6).

Note: You can clear an existing statistical drawing by
pressing $\boxed{\text{2nd}}$ [DRAW] and selecting ⟨ClrDraw⟩.

**Plotting the
Data**

To view a graph of the statistical data you entered, begin
on a blank line on the Home screen or program edit
screen.

1. Press $\boxed{\text{2nd}}$ [STAT] $\boxed{\blacktriangleright}$ to display the STAT DRAW menu.

2. Choose the type of drawing you want:

   - To draw a histogram, select ⟨Hist⟩.

   - To draw a scatter plot of the points, select ⟨Scatter⟩.

   - To plot the data points connected with a line, select
     ⟨xyLine⟩.

   The appropriate instruction is copied to the current
   cursor location.

3. Press $\boxed{\text{ENTER}}$ to complete the instruction.

When the instruction is executed, the plot is displayed.

Histogram

Hist draws one-variable data as bar charts. It uses the RANGE variable **Xscl** to define the numerical width of the bars. A data value on the edge of a bar is counted in the bar immediately to the right.

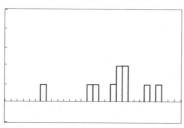

Scatter Plot

Scatter draws each data point as a coordinate on the display.

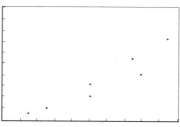

Line Drawing

xyLine draws the data points as coordinates on the display in the order they are in the data list and connects the points with a line. You may want to use **xSort** to sort the data first.

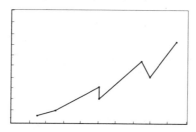

Storing and Recalling a Data Value

For advanced applications, such as programming, values can be stored to or recalled from individual statistical data points on the Home screen or from a program.

Storing to a Statistical Data Point

To store to a statistical data point, begin on a blank line on the Home screen or program edit screen.

1. Enter the value you want to store. This value can be an expression.

2. Press $\boxed{\text{STO}\blacktriangleright}$.

3. Press $\boxed{\text{2nd}}$ [{x}] or $\boxed{\text{2nd}}$ [{y}].

   {x}(or {y}(is copied to the current cursor location.

4. Enter the number (can be an expression) of the data point where you want the value stored, and then press $\boxed{)}$.

   Note: You can store no more than one location past the current last data point. The number of the last data point is in the variable **DIM**{x} on the VARS DIM menu.

5. Press $\boxed{\text{ENTER}}$ to complete the instruction.

When the instruction is executed, the TI–81 stores the value to the data point.

Using a Statistical Data Point

To use a statistical data point in an expression:

1. Press $\boxed{\text{2nd}}$ [{x}] or $\boxed{\text{2nd}}$ [{y}].

   {x}(or {y}(is copied to the current cursor location.

2. Enter the expression for the number of the data point you want to reference, and then press $\boxed{)}$.

3. Continue entering the expression.

Example: Analyzing One-Variable Statistics

Calculate the one-variable statistical results for the scores on a class quiz.

Problem

On a quiz, the class members earned scores of 76, 89, 88, 96, 90, 94, 90, 84, 85, and 89. Calculate the mean and standard deviation.

Solution

1. Press [2nd] [STAT] [◀] to display the STAT DATA menu. Select ⟨Edit⟩ and enter the class scores as one-variable data.

   Notice that two people scored 90, and two scored 89. Enter these with a frequency of 2. All others can use the default frequency of 1.

x1=76	y1=1
x2=89	y2=2
x3=88	y3=1
x4=96	y4=1
x5=90	y5=2
x6=94	y6=1
x7=84	y7=1
x8=85	y8=1

2. Press [2nd] [STAT] to display the STAT CALC menu. Select ⟨1-Var⟩. The instruction **1-Var** is copied to the Home screen.

3. Press [ENTER] to execute the instruction. The results are displayed.

   ```
   1-Var
    x̄=88.1
    Σx=881
    Σx²=77895
    Sx=5.566766466
    σx=5.281098371
    n=10
   ```

Example: Analyzing Two-Variable Statistics

Problem

The number of buildings of more than 12 stories found in a sampling of cities is:

Population	Buildings
150,000	4
250,000	9
500,000	31
500,000	20
750,000	55
800,000	42
950,000	73

How many buildings of more than 12 stories would you expect to find in a city of 300,000 people based on the observed data?

Solution

1. Press 2nd [STAT] ◀ to display the STAT DATA menu. Select ⟨Edit⟩ and enter the data points. The number of buildings is the dependent variable and should be entered as Y.

2. Press 2nd [STAT]. Select and execute each of the regression models in turn. Record the value of r each time.

3. Press 2nd [STAT]. Execute the power regression model since it gave the value of r closest to the absolute value of 1.

4. Store 300,000 into the variable X.

5. Press VARS. Select the LR menu. Select ⟨RegEQ⟩ to copy the regression equation

   4.874211472E−8X ^ 1.529413355

   to the Home screen.

6. Press ENTER. The prediction, based on the observed data, is that a city of 300,000 people would have 12 (11.60611211 rounded) buildings taller than 12 stories.

Chapter 8: Programming

This chapter describes the programming features of the TI–81.

Chapter Contents

The PRGM (Program) Menus

Pressing PRGM from anywhere other than the program edit screen accesses the program operations. The operations are grouped functionally in three menus: executing a program, editing a program, and erasing a program.

The PRGM Menu

Menu	Meaning
EXEC EDIT ERASE	
1: Prgm1 *title*	Executes program 1
2: Prgm2 *title*	Executes program 2
3: Prgm3	(etc.)
4: Prgm4	
. . .	Programs 5 through 0, A through Z, θ
EXEC **EDIT** ERASE	
1: Prgm1 *title*	Enters or edits program 1
2: Prgm2 *title*	Enters or edits program 2
3: Prgm3	(etc.)
4: Prgm4	
. . .	Programs 5 through 0, A through Z, θ
EXEC EDIT **ERASE**	
1: Prgm1 *size*	Erases program 1
2: Prgm2 *size*	Erases program 2
3: Prgm3	(etc.)
4: Prgm4	
. . .	Programs 5 through 0, A through Z, θ

Notes about the PRGM Menus

The current menu name and item number are highlighted.

When you select a program name from the EXEC menu, the program name is copied to the Home screen.

When you select a program name from the EDIT menu, the program edit screen for that program appears.

When you select a program name from the ERASE menu, the ERASE menu appears.

General Notes about Programming

The TI-81 can store up to 37 programs. The Constant Memory™ feature retains the programs when the TI-81 is turned off.

While Entering or Editing a Program

A program consists of program commands. A program command can be an expression or an instruction.

A colon indicates the beginning of each program command. A command may be longer than one line on the screen; if so, it will wrap to the next screen line.

You can include variables, functions, graphing activities, and matrix or statistical calculations in programs.

When you access another menu, it replaces the program edit screen temporarily until you select an item.

Pressing PRGM from the program edit screen displays a set of menus containing programming instructions (see page 8-9).

The memory used to store programs is shared with statistical data. If there is no stored statistical data, you can store programs occupying a total of 2400 bytes. The memory status is displayed on the RESET screen (see page 1-28). If you run out of memory, you can free additional memory by clearing the statistical data (see page 7-3) or erasing a program.

The TI-81 checks for errors during execution, not as you enter or edit the program.

While a Program Is Executing

Variables are global. Storing a value to a variable from a program changes the value in memory at the time of execution.

Programs update the variable **Ans** during execution, just as expressions do on the Home screen.

Programs do not update Last Entry as each command is executed.

Entering a Program

In general, any command that can be copied to and executed from the Home screen can be included in a program. A sample program is shown on page 8-14. Additional programs are given in Chapter 9. The Table of Commands in Appendix A is a convenient reference showing key sequences and correct formats for programming instructions.

Selecting a Program

To select the program you want to enter:

1. Press PRGM ▶ to display the PRGM EDIT menu.

2. Select the number, letter, or character of the program you want to enter or edit. The programs are identified as 1 through 0, A through Z, and θ. For example, press 1 for Program 1 or ALPHA [Z] for Program Z.

The program edit screen appears:

```
Prgm1 :
     :
```

Entering a Program

To assign a title to the program and enter program commands in a program:

1. Enter a descriptive title of up to 8 characters (letters, numbers, θ, and decimal point). This title helps you identify the program in the future.

   Note: For your convenience, the TI-81 keyboard is set automatically for alpha-lock. To enter a digit as part of the title, press ALPHA to cancel alpha-lock.

2. Press ENTER.

   The cursor moves to the first line of the program. A colon indicates the beginning of the command.

3. Enter the first program command. Then press ENTER.

   The cursor moves to the next program command line. A colon indicates the beginning of the command.

4. Enter the next program command. Continue until you have entered all commands in the program.

Notes about Entering Program Commands	Begin each program command on a new line, immediately following the colon.

In addition to the special program commands described in this chapter, any command that can be copied to and executed from the Home screen can be included in a program. You cannot use ZOOM or TRACE to explore a graph from a program.

To copy the last entry made on the Home screen into a program, press 2nd [ENTRY], just as on the Home screen.

The TI–81 supplies an implied **End** following the last program command that you enter.

Leaving the Program Edit Screen	When you finish entering or editing a program, you must leave the program edit screen in order to execute the program.

Leave the program edit screen in one of the following ways:

- Select another screen by pressing the appropriate key, such as GRAPH.

- Press 2nd [QUIT] to return to the Home screen.

Editing a Program

Once a program is entered, it can be changed.

Editing a Program Command

To edit a program command:

1. If the program edit screen is not displayed, press PRGM ▶ to display the PRGM EDIT menu. Then select the program you want to edit. The program edit screen is displayed.

2. Use ▲ or ▼ to move the cursor to the program command you want to change.

3. Change the program command:

   - Use ▶ or ◀ to position the cursor over the symbol you want to change. Then type over it or use INS or DEL to change it.

   - Press CLEAR to erase the current program command. Then enter a new program command.

Inserting a Program Command

To insert a program command on the program edit screen:

1. Use the cursor-movement keys:

   - To insert a new line below it, place the cursor at the end of a program command.

   - To insert a new line above it, place the cursor at the beginning of a program command.

2. Press INS ENTER and a blank line is inserted.

3. Enter a new program command on the blank line. If you need to get out of insert, press INS again.

Deleting a Program Command

To delete a program command from the program edit screen:

1. Use ▲ or ▼ to move the cursor to the program command that you want to delete.

2. Press CLEAR and the program command is cleared.

3. Press DEL and the line is deleted.

Executing a Program

To execute a program, copy the program name from the PRGM
EXEC menu to the Home screen, and then press ENTER.

**Executing a
Program from
the Home Screen**

To execute a program, begin on a blank line on the Home
screen.

1. Press PRGM to display the PRGM EXEC menu.

2. Select the number, letter, or character of the program
   you want to execute.

   The name of the program is copied to the Home
   screen.

3. Press ENTER to complete the instruction and begin
   execution of the program.

   While the program is executing, the busy indicator is
   displayed. If the program does not produce any
   output, or if an **Input** variable command was executed
   subsequently, the message **Done** is displayed when the
   program completes execution.

**"Breaking" a
Program**

ON acts as a break during program execution. Press and
hold ON until the program stops. When you press ON to
stop program execution, the error screen is displayed.

- To go to the program edit screen, press 1.

- To go to the Home screen, press 2.

Erasing a Program

To erase a program, select the name of the program from the
PRGM ERASE menu.

**Selecting and
Erasing a
Program**

To select the program you want to erase:

1. Press PRGM ◄ to display the PRGM ERASE menu.

   The size of each program appears next to the program
   name.

2. Select the number, letter, or character of the program
   you want to erase.

   The ERASE Prgm menu appears. The title that you
   entered to describe the program appears on the top
   line.

   ```
   Prgmn title
   1:Do not erase
   2:Erase
   ```

3. Make the appropriate menu selection:

   • If you do not want to erase the program, press 1 to
     select ⟨Do not erase⟩.

     You are returned to the Home screen.

   • If you want to erase the program, press 2 to select
     ⟨Erase⟩.

     The program is erased immediately and you are
     returned to the Home screen.

Accessing the Programming Instructions Menus

Pressing PRGM from the program edit screen accesses the programming instructions. The programming instructions are grouped functionally in three menus: control instructions, input/output instructions, and execute instructions.

The PRGM Instructions Menus

Menu	Meaning
CTL I/O EXEC	
1:Lbl	Defines a label
2:Goto	Goes to a label
3:If	Begins an If instruction
4:IS>(	Increments and skips if greater than
5:DS<(	Decrements and skips if less than
6:Pause	Pauses to display the screen
7:End	Ends the program
8:Stop	Stops execution
CTL **I/O** EXEC	
1:Disp	Displays text or a value on the screen
2:Input	Lets you input during execution
3:DispHome	Displays the Home screen
4:DispGraph	Displays the graph screen
5:ClrHome	Clears the Home screen
CTL I/O **EXEC**	
1:Prgm1 *title*	Executes program 1 as a subroutine
2:Prgm2 *title*	Executes program 2 as a subroutine
3:Prgm3	(etc.)
4:Prgm4	
. . .	Programs 5 through 0, A through Z, θ

Notes about the PRGM Instructions Menus

The current menu name and item number are highlighted.

Notice that these PRGM menus, which you can access only from the program edit screen, contain instructions that are used only in programming.

When you select an instruction from the CTL menu or the I/O menu, the instruction is copied to the current cursor location.

When you select a program name from the EXEC menu, the name of the program is copied to the current cursor location on the program edit screen.

Begin each instruction on a new program command line.

The Control Instructions

The PRGM CTL (control) instructions direct the flow within an executing program. These instructions are on the PRGM CTL menu, which you access from the program edit screen.

The Lbl and Goto Instructions

The **Lbl** (label) and **Goto** instructions are used together for branching.

Lbl has one argument, which assigns a label to a program command. A label is a single letter, number, or θ. The labels A through Z and θ are independent of the variables A through Z and θ.

The completed instruction is:

Lbl *label*

Goto has one argument, a label to which to branch. The instruction transfers control to that label.

The completed instruction is:

Goto *label*

The If Instruction

The **If** instruction is used for testing, looping, and branching. It has one argument. The argument is an expression, usually a relational test (see pages 2–9 and 2–10).

If the argument evaluates to zero (the test is not true), the next program command is skipped. If the argument is nonzero (the test is true), the program continues execution with the next command.

The completed instruction is:

If *expression*

For example:

If A>B	If A is greater than B,
A→J	store A in J; then go to Lbl Q.
Goto Q	If not, do not store A in J; go to Lbl Q.

**The IS>
Instruction**

The IS>((increment-and-skip) instruction has two arguments, separated by a comma. The first argument is a variable name. The second argument is a value or expression, followed by a close parenthesis. The instruction evaluates the second argument and then adds 1 to the value of the variable in the first argument. If the first argument is greater than the second argument, the next program command is skipped.

The completed instruction is:

IS>(*variable*,*expression*)

**The DS<
Instruction**

The DS<((decrement-and-skip) instruction has two arguments, separated by a comma. The first argument is a variable name. The second argument is a value or expression, followed by a close parenthesis. The instruction evaluates the second argument and then subtracts 1 from the value of the variable in the first argument. If the first argument is less than the second argument, the next program command is skipped.

The completed instruction is:

DS<(*variable*,*expression*)

**The Pause
Instruction**

The **Pause** instruction suspends execution of the program until you press ENTER. This allows time for you to see results or view graphs that are displayed on the screen.

**The End
Instruction**

The **End** instruction identifies the logical end of program commands in an executing program. When **End** is encountered within a program that was called from another, control returns to the calling program.

It is not necessary to enter an **End** instruction at the end of a program. There is an implied (or hidden) **End** at the end of each program.

**The Stop
Instruction**

The **Stop** instruction stops execution of a program and returns you to the Home screen.

The Input/Output Instructions

The PRGM I/O instructions control input to and output from a program. These instructions are on the PRGM I/O menu, which you access from the program edit screen.

The Disp Instruction

The **Disp** instruction displays text messages or the current value of a variable from a program. You must precede and follow the text message with quotes (″). The space key (⇥) and ? can be used in text messages.

Text display begins on the left side of the screen. You can display more than 16 characters in a message; the message "wraps" to the beginning of the next line.

The current value of a variable is displayed on the right side of the screen.

If **Pause** (see page 8–11) is the next program command, the program halts temporarily and allows you to examine the screen. Execution resumes when you press ENTER.

For example, from the program edit screen:

Procedure	Keystrokes	Display
Enter **Display**	PRGM ▶ ⟨Disp⟩	:Disp
Begin text	ALPHA [″] ALPHA [K]	:Disp "K
Enter = sign	2nd [TEST] ⟨ = ⟩ ALPHA [″] ENTER	:Disp "K="
Enter **Display**	PRGM ▶ ⟨Disp⟩	:Disp
Enter variable	ALPHA [K] ENTER	:Disp K
Enter **Pause**	PRGM ⟨Pause⟩ ENTER	:Pause

On execution, these commands display, for example:

```
K=
        123.4567
```

The Input Instruction	The **Input** instruction may or may not have an argument:
	• If it has an argument, it is used to store a value to a variable during program execution.
	• If it does not have an argument, it is used to explore a graph during program execution.
The Input Instruction with Variables	When the **Input** instruction has an argument, the argument is a variable name.
	The TI–81 prompts with a **?** during execution. You must enter a value and then press ENTER. The value you enter is stored to that variable and the program resumes execution.
	To display the variable name as a prompt during execution, use the **Disp** instruction.
The Input Instruction with Graphing	When the **Input** instruction has no argument, it automatically displays the current graph when the instruction is executed.
	You can move the free-moving cursor, which updates the X and Y variables in Rectangular mode or R and θ in Polar mode. Press ENTER to resume program execution.
The DispHome Instruction	The **DispHome** instruction displays the Home screen from a program.
The DispGraph Instruction	The **DispGraph** instruction displays a graph of currently selected functions from within a program. There is no cursor on the graph.
	If **Pause** (see page 8–11) is the next program command, the program halts temporarily and allows you to examine the screen. Execution resumes when you press ENTER.
The ClrHome Instruction	The **ClrHome** instruction clears the Home screen from a program.

Sample Program

The sample program below saves the RANGE variables from the current graph and allows you to recall those settings at a later time. It illustrates several types of programming commands that are presented in this chapter.

The Problem

Save the settings for the current viewing rectangle so that you can return to them quickly after zooming or changing the RANGE variables.

This program prompts you to save the current RANGE variables or to recall the saved variables. The six RANGE variables are saved in the variables A through F.

The Solution

PrgmA:RANGESAV	Title of program
:Disp "ENTER 1 TO SAVE OR 2 TO RECALL, THEN PRESS ENTER"	Display a message
:Input Z	"Get" the key press
:If Z=2	If you chose Recall, then
:Goto 1	skip to Recall section
:Xmin→A	Save RANGE variables
:Xmax→B	
:Xscl→C	
:Ymin→D	
:Ymax→E	
:Yscl→F	
:End	Quit executing program
:Lbl 1	Begin Recall section
:A→Xmin	Set RANGE variables to saved
:B→Xmax	values
:C→Xscl	
:D→Ymin	
:E→Ymax	
:F→Yscl	
:DispGraph	Display new viewing rectangle
:End	

**Program
Features**

Generally, you can do the same tasks from a TI–81 program that you can do interactively on the calculator. There are special programming instructions to perform interactive tasks, such as decision-making, setting modes, defining RANGE variables, and selecting functions to graph.

The programming language on the TI–81 is very similar to other programming languages.

- Control instructions control the order in which program statements are executed. In the sample program, **If, Goto, Lbl**, and **End** control the program flow. The commands for controlling program flow are in the CTL menu and are described on pages 8–10 and 8–11.

- Output instructions display messages, values, and graphs during program execution. Input instructions accept input from the user. In the sample program, **Disp** and **DispGraph** display information and **Input** allows the user to indicate a choice. The commands for displaying and for inputting are in the I/O menu and are described on pages 8–12 and 8–13.

- Values are stored to variables in programs with the STO▸ key, just as on the Home screen.

Calling Other Programs (The Execute Instructions)

On the TI-81, any program can be executed as a program or called from another program to function as a subroutine. The PRGM EXEC menu accesses the instruction that calls another program as a subroutine.

Calling a Program from Another Program

To call one program from another:

1. From the program edit screen, press PRGM ◄ to display the PRGM EXEC menu.

2. Select the number, letter, or character of the program you want to execute as a subroutine.

   The name of the program is copied to the current cursor location on the program edit screen.

When this program command is encountered during program execution, the next command that the TI-81 executes is the first command in the second program. It returns to the subsequent command in the first program only when it encounters an **End** instruction in the second program.

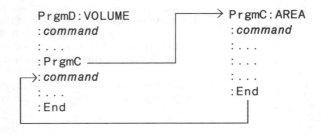

```
PrgmD:VOLUME          ──→ PrgmC:AREA
:command                  :command
:...                      :...
:PrgmC ──────────┘        :...
:command                  :...
:...                      :End
:End
```

Notes about Calling Programs

Variables are global. The same variable name in two programs accesses the same location in memory. When you store a new value to a variable from a program, it is changed in memory. Any other programs using that variable also recall the new value.

The **Goto** and **Lbl** arguments are local to the program in which they are located. A label in one program is not "known" by another program. You cannot use a **Goto** instruction to branch to a label in another program.

Setting Modes from a Program

Pressing MODE from the program edit screen accesses the MODE menus. The MODE operations are grouped functionally into two menus: numeric display and graph display.

The MODE Menu

Menu	Meaning
NUMBER GRAPH	
1 : Norm	Normal display format
2 : Sci	Scientific display format
3 : Eng	Engineering display format
4 : Fix	Fixed decimal display setting
5 : Float	Floating decimal display setting
6 : Rad	Radian angle setting
7 : Deg	Degree angle setting
NUMBER **GRAPH**	
1 : Function	Function graphing
2 : Param	Parametric graphing
3 : Connected	Connected line graph
4 : Dot	Dot graph
5 : Sequence	Sequential plotting
6 : Simul	Simultaneous plotting
7 : Grid Off	Graph grid off
8 : Grid On	Graph grid on
9 : Rect	Rectangular coordinate display
0 : Polar	Polar coordinate display

Notes about the MODE Menus

The current menu name and item number are highlighted.

Notice that these MODE menus, which you can access only from the program edit screen, are different from the MODE screen described in Chapter 1.

Begin on a blank line. When you select a mode from these MODE menus, the name of the mode is copied to the current cursor location.

If you select ⟨Fix⟩, you also must enter a number between 0 and 9 as an argument to indicate the number of decimal places.

Chapter 9: Applications

This chapter contains twelve problems that incorporate features described in the preceding chapters. Seven of the examples are worked from the Home screen. Five of the examples use programs.

Chapter Contents

Solving a System of Linear Equations

You can use the matrix arithmetic features of the TI–81 to solve systems of linear equations with up to six unknown variables. Determine a matrix representation of a system of four equations with four unknowns. Then use the matrix model to solve the system.

Problem

Solve the system of equations below by creating matrix [A] containing the coefficients of the variables in the equations and matrix [C] containing the constant values. Then solve the equivalent matrix representation [A][X] = [C] for [X].

$$
\begin{aligned}
x \quad - z - 2w &= -26 \\
8x + y - 6z + 2w &= 75 \\
-3x + 4y + z \quad &= 38 \\
2x + 2y \quad - 3w &= 8
\end{aligned}
\qquad
\begin{bmatrix}
1 & 0 & -1 & -2 \\
8 & 1 & -6 & 2 \\
-3 & 4 & 1 & 0 \\
2 & 2 & 0 & -3
\end{bmatrix}
\begin{bmatrix}
x \\ y \\ z \\ w
\end{bmatrix}
=
\begin{bmatrix}
-26 \\ 75 \\ 38 \\ 8
\end{bmatrix}
$$

Solution

1. Press MATRX . Select the EDIT menu. Set the dimensions to 4×4 and enter the following elements into matrix [A]:

   ```
    1  0 -1 -2
    8  1 -6  2
   -3  4  1  0
    2  2  0 -3
   ```

2. Press MATRX . Select the EDIT menu. Set the dimensions to 4×1 and enter the following elements into matrix [C]:

   ```
   -26
    75
    38
     8
   ```

3. Press 2nd [QUIT] to return to the Home screen.

4. Since [X] = [A]⁻¹[C], enter the expression

   [A]⁻¹[C]

5. Press ENTER to execute the instruction.

   The result matrix [X] is displayed and stored in **Ans**.

[10]	Thus,	x = 10
[15]		y = 15
[8]		z = 8
[14]		w = 14

Solving a System of Nonlinear Equations

Use the graphing feature of the TI-81 to solve a system of two nonlinear equations.

Problem

Using the ZOOM features, determine how many solutions exist and what the solutions are for the system

$$Y = 17 - X^2$$
$$Y = X^3 + X$$

Solution

1. Press $\boxed{Y=}$. Enter the equations as functions in the Y= list.

2. Press $\boxed{ZOOM}$. Select ⟨Standard⟩ to graph the functions in the standard default viewing rectangle. There are no apparent solutions in this rectangle.

3. To display more of the graph, press $\boxed{ZOOM}$. Select ⟨Zoom Out⟩. Press $\boxed{ENTER}$ to zoom out around the center of the display. There appears to be only one solution.

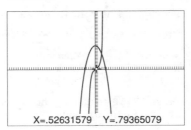

X=.52631579   Y=.79365079

4. Press $\boxed{ZOOM}$. Select ⟨Zoom In⟩. Move the cursor to the apparent intersection of the functions. Press $\boxed{ENTER}$ to zoom in on the intersection.

5. Move the cursor until you think you have placed it exactly over the intersection. Note the values for X and Y displayed at the bottom of the screen. Press $\boxed{ENTER}$ to zoom in on the graph again.

6. Repeat step 5 until you are satisfied with the accuracy of the solution.

Graphing a Piecewise Defined Function

Using relational operators, graph a piecewise defined function whose characteristics differ over certain values of X.

Problem

A parking garage charges $1.50 for the first half hour for parking. It charges 60 cents per additional half hour (or fraction thereof), with a maximum of $8 per day. How long can you park for $3? For $5?

The function consists of four segments, where Y is the parking charge in dollars and X is the time in hours.

Y = 1.50	for	$0 < X \le .5$
Y = 1.50 + .60 Int (2X)	for	$.5 < X < 5.5)$
Y = 8.00	for	$5.5 \le X$

Using relational operators, these segments can be combined into the single function

$1.5(0<X)(X \le .5)+(1.5+.6abs(Int(-2X)+1))(.5<X)(X \le 5.5)+8(5.5<X)$

Solution

1. Press MODE. Select ⟨Dot⟩ when graphing piecewise functions.

2. Press Y= . Enter the expression to define Y1.

3. Press RANGE. Change the RANGE variable values.

Xmin = 0	Ymin = 0	Xres = 1
Xmax = 9.5	Ymax = 9	
Xscl = 1	Yscl = 1	

4. Press TRACE to display the graph. Use TRACE to determine the answers.

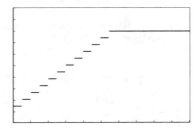

Note: When any portion of a piecewise function is undefined at a value of X ($\sqrt{x}$ for x<0, for example), the entire function is undefined at that value. Break the piecewise function into more than one Y= function.

Exploring End Behavior of a Rational Function

Graphically determine the end behavior of a rational function. End behavior is the behavior of the function when |X| is large.

Problem

Graph the function

$$Y = (X^3 - 10X^2 + X + 50)/(X - 2)$$

Observe that the end behavior of the function is very similar to the behavior of the function

$$Y = X^2$$

Solution

1. Press $\boxed{\text{MODE}}$. Select the default modes.

2. Press $\boxed{\text{Y=}}$. Enter the expression to define Y1.

3. Press $\boxed{\text{ZOOM}}$. Select ⟨Standard⟩ to graph the functions in the standard default viewing rectangle.

4. Press $\boxed{\text{ZOOM}}$. Select ⟨Set Factors⟩. Set **XFact** to 5 and **YFact** to 25.

5. Press $\boxed{\text{RANGE}}$. Set **Xscl** and **Yscl** to 0 to eliminate the tick marks along the axes.

6. Press $\boxed{\text{ZOOM}}$. Select ⟨Zoom Out⟩. Leave the cursor positioned at the center of the graph and press $\boxed{\text{ENTER}}$.

7. Press $\boxed{\text{ENTER}}$ to zoom out again.

8. To see the effect on the RANGE variables, press $\boxed{\text{RANGE}}$ and notice the new values for **Xmin**, **Xmax**, **Ymin**, and **Ymax**.

9. Press $\boxed{\text{2nd}}$ [DRAW]. Select ⟨DrawF⟩. Enter the expression X^2 and press $\boxed{\text{ENTER}}$.

The function X^2 is drawn on the graph with the original function Y1. Notice that the end behavior of the original function is very similar to X^2.

Analyzing Statistical Data Graphically

Use the graphing features of the TI-81 to examine a statistical analysis.

Problem

Using the statistical analysis problem defined on page 7–18, copy each regression equation to the Y= list. Then plot the data points on a scatter plot.

Solution

1. Enter the data as described on page 7–18.

2. From a blank line on the Home screen, press [2nd] [STAT], select ⟨LinReg⟩, and then press [ENTER] to perform a linear regression analysis.

3. Press [Y=]. If necessary, press [CLEAR] to clear the expression in Y1. Press [VARS], select the LR menu, and then select ⟨RegEQ⟩ to copy the regression equation to Y1.

4. Repeat steps 2 and 3 for **LnReg** and Y2, **ExpReg** and Y3, and **PwrReg** and Y4.

5. Press [RANGE]. Set the RANGE variables to:

Xmin = 0	Ymin = 0	Xres = 1
Xmax = 1000000	Ymax = 100	
Xscl = 100000	Yscl = 10	

6. Press [2nd] [STAT]. Select the DRAW menu. Select ⟨Scatter⟩ and then press [ENTER] to plot the statistical data and the regression curves.

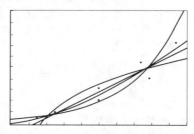

Determining Maximum Volume of an Open Box

Calculate the maximum volume of an open box graphically.

Problem

Fold a sheet of cardboard to form a box of maximum volume by removing squares of equal size from each corner. If the cardboard is L by W and the sides of the squares are X, the formula for the volume (V) of the box is

$$V = (L - 2X)(W - 2X)X$$

Specifically, calculate the maximum volume possible for a box constructed from a sheet 8.5″ by 11.0″.

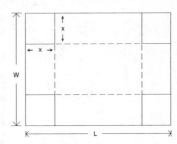

Solution

1. Press [Y=]. Enter the expression to define Y1. Use

   (11 − 2X) (8.5 − 2X) X

2. Consider the domain of X. An X less than 0 or greater than 4.25 cannot occur in this real-life problem, although the function is defined for values less than 0 or greater than 4.25. Likewise, any values of Y (volume) less than 0 are not possible.

   Press [RANGE]. Change the RANGE variables.

Xmin = 0	Ymin = 0	Xres = 1
Xmax = 4.25	Ymax = 100	
Xscl = 1	Yscl = 10	

3. Press [GRAPH] to display the function.

4. Press [TRACE]. Move the cursor along the function until you have identified the maximum value of Y (volume). You can zoom in to obtain desired accuracy.

5. With the cursor on the maximum value of Y (volume), press [2nd] [QUIT] to return to the Home screen. Enter **8.5 − 2X** and press [ENTER] to determine the length of one side of the box. Enter **11 − 2X** and press [ENTER] to determine the length of the other side. X is the height of the box.

Simulating Motion with Parametric Equations

Use two pairs of parametric equations to describe two different objects in motion. Determine when the two objects are closest.

Problem

The first object in motion is a person riding on a ferris wheel. The ferris wheel has a diameter of 40 feet and is rotating counterclockwise at a rate of one revolution every 12 seconds. The following parametric equation describes the location of the person on the ferris wheel, where T is time, r is the radius, α is the angle of rotation, s is the time for one revolution, the bottom center of the ferris wheel is (0,0), and the passenger is at the rightmost point (20, 20) when T = 0.

$X(T) = r \cos \alpha$ where $\alpha = 2\pi T/s$
$Y(T) = r + r \sin \alpha$

The second object in motion is a ball thrown from a height even with the bottom of the ferris wheel, but at a distance (d) of 75 feet to the right of the bottom center of the ferris wheel. The ball is thrown with a velocity (v_0) of 60 feet per second at an angle (θ) of 60° from the horizontal. The following parametric equation describes the location of the ball, using the same parameter (time T) as the ferris wheel.

$X(T) = d - T v_0 \cos \theta$
$Y(T) = T v_0 \sin \theta - 16 T^2$

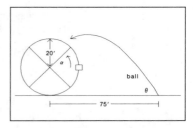

Solution

1. Press $\boxed{\text{MODE}}$. Select ⟨Rad⟩, ⟨Param⟩, and ⟨Simul⟩. Simultaneous mode simulates what is happening with the two objects in motion over time.

2. Press $\boxed{\text{RANGE}}$. Set the RANGE variables appropriately for this real-life problem.

Tmin = 0	Xmin = −20	Ymin = 0
Tmax = 12	Xmax = 80	Ymax = 67
Tstep = .1	Xscl = 10	Yscl = 10

**Solution
(Continued)**

3. Press $\boxed{Y=}$. Enter the expressions to define both parametric equations.

   X1T= 20cos (πT/6)
   Y1T= 20+20sin (πT/6)
   X2T= 75−60Tcos 60°
   Y2T= 60Tsin 60°−16T²

4. Press $\boxed{\text{GRAPH}}$ to graph the equations and watch closely as they are plotted. Notice that the ball and the passenger on the ferris wheel appear to be closest at a time when they are near where the paths cross in the upper right quadrant of the ferris wheel.

5. Press $\boxed{\text{RANGE}}$. Change the RANGE variable values to concentrate on this portion of the graph.

Tmin = 0	Xmin = 0	Ymin = 20
Tmax = 3	Xmax = 20	Ymax = 45
Tstep = .02	Xscl = 1	Yscl = 1

6. Press $\boxed{\text{TRACE}}$. After the graph is plotted, press $\boxed{\blacktriangleright}$ to move near the point on the ferris wheel where the paths cross. Note the values of X, Y, and T.

7. Press $\boxed{\blacktriangledown}$ to move to the other curve. Note the values of X and Y (T is unchanged). Notice where the cursor is located. This is the position of the ball when the person on the ferris wheel passes the intersection.

   Press $\boxed{\blacktriangleright}$ to move the cursor along the curve of the ball to the intersection, and then press $\boxed{\blacktriangledown}$. This is the passenger's position at this time.

   Using the TRACE feature of the TI–81, you can, in effect, take "snapshots" in time to explore the relative behavior of two objects in motion.

Graphing the Inverse of a Relation

You can use the parametric graphing feature of the TI-81 to graph the inverse relation of any function by defining the function in X₁T and Y₁T and its inverse in X₂T and Y₂T.

Problem

Graph the inverse of the function $Y = X^3 - 2X + 3$.

Any function that can be plotted in function graphing can be plotted in parametric graphing by defining the X component as T and the Y component as F(T).

$X_1T = T$
$Y_1T = T^3 - 2T + 3$

Solution

1. Press MODE. Select ⟨Param⟩ and ⟨Simul⟩.

2. Press RANGE. Change the RANGE variable values.

Tmin = −10	Xmin = −15	Ymin = −10
Tmax = 10	Xmax = 15	Ymax = 10
Tstep =.1	Xscl = 1	Yscl = 1

3. Press Y=. Enter the expressions to define the parametric equation.

   X1T = T
   Y1T = T³ − 2T + 3

4. Enter the expressions to define the inverse.

   X2T = T³ − 2T + 3
   Y2T = T

5. Enter the expressions to define the line Y = X, about which the graph of the function and the graph of its inverse are symmetric. That is, the reflection of the graph of the function through the line Y = X produces the graph of its inverse.

   X3T = T
   Y3T = T

6. Press TRACE. The graph is plotted. Press ▶ several times, press ▼, and then press ▲. The cursor moves from a point on the relation to the reflected point and back.

Note: The expressions to define the inverse can be generalized.

$X_2T = Y_1T$
$Y_2T = X_1T$

Graphing the Unit Circle and Trigonometric Curves

You can use the parametric graphing feature of the TI–81 to show the relationship between the unit circle and any trigonometric curve.

Problem

Graph the unit circle and the sine curve to demonstrate graphically the relationship between them.

Any function that can be plotted in function graphing can be plotted in parametric graphing by defining the X component as T and the Y component as F(T).

Solution

1. Press MODE. Select ⟨Rad⟩, ⟨Param⟩, and ⟨Simul⟩.

2. Press RANGE. Change the RANGE variable values.

Tmin = 0	Xmin = −2	Ymin = −3
Tmax = 6.28	Xmax = 6.28	Ymax = 3
Tstep =.1	Xscl = 1.57	Yscl = 1

3. Press Y=. Enter the expressions to define the unit circle.

   X1T= −1+cos T
   Y1T= sin T

4. Enter the expressions to define the sine curve.

   X2T=T
   Y2T= sin T

5. Press TRACE. The graph is plotted. Press ◄ several times to move the cursor along the unit circle. Press ▼ to move the cursor to the sine curve.

   This "unwraps" the sine function from the unit circle.

   Note: The "unwrapping" can be generalized. Replace sin T in Y2T with any other trig function to "unwrap" that function.

Program: Numerical Solve Routine

This program uses the Newton-Raphson method to find the roots (zeros) of a function numerically.

Problem

Use the graphing features of the TI–81 to find the roots of a function.

Specifically, calculate the solution to the equation

$e^x - 3x = 0$

Solution

The procedure consists of:

- Graphing the function $f(x) = e^x - 3x$.

- Using the TRACE feature to identify the first approximation of a root graphically.

- Iteratively refining the root estimation in a program.

1. Enter the program.

```
Prgm1:NEWTON
:(Xmax-Xmin)/100      Initialize delta for NDeriv
→D
:1→I                  Initialize counter
:Lbl 1                Begin loop
:X-Y1/NDeriv(Y1,        Calculate a new root
D)→R
:If abs (X-R)≤ab      Test
s (X/1E10)
:Goto 2
:R→X                  Use root as new estimate
:I+1→I                Increment counter
:Goto 1               End loop
:Lbl 2
:Disp "ROOT="         Display root
:Disp R
:Disp "ITER="         Display number of iterations
:Disp I
```

Solution
(Continued)

2. Return to the Home screen by pressing [2nd] [QUIT]. Press [MODE]. Select the default modes.

3. Press [Y=]. Enter the expression to define Y1. Use

   e^X−3X

4. Press [ZOOM]. Select ⟨Standard⟩ to graph the function in the standard default viewing rectangle.

5. Press [TRACE]. Move the cursor to one of the roots. The variables X and Y are updated as you move the cursor.

6. From a blank line on the Home screen, press [PRGM]. Select ⟨Prgm1⟩ and then press [ENTER] to execute the program.

7. Press [TRACE]. Move the cursor to the other root.

8. From a blank line on the Home screen, press [ENTER] to execute the program again.

   The results are:

   ```
   ROOT=
              .6190612867
    ITER=
                        6
   ROOT=
             1.512134552
    ITER=
                        8
   ```

Program: Numerical Integration

This program uses Simpson's method to estimate the definite integral of a function.

Problem

Estimate the definite integral

$$\int_0^1 (6 - 6x^5)\,dx$$

Solution

1. Enter the program.

```
Prgm2:SIMPSON
:All-Off                      Turn off all functions
:Disp "LOWER LIM             Input lower limit
IT"
:Input A
:Disp "UPPER LIM             Input upper limit
IT"
:Input B
:Disp "N DIVISIO             Input number of divisions
NS"
:Input D
:0→S                         Initialize sum of areas
:(B-A)/2D→W                  Calculate width of division
:1→J                         Initialize counter
:Lbl 1                       Begin loop
:A+2(J-1)W→L                   Calculate left point
:A+2JW→R                       Calculate right point
:(L+R)/2→M                     Calculate middle point
:L→X
:Y1→L                        Value of function at left
:M→X
:Y1→M                        Value of function at middle
:R→X
:Y1→R                        Value of function at right
:W(L+4M+R)/3+S→S             Sum of areas
:IS>(J,D)
:Goto 1                      End loop
:Disp "AREA="                Display result
:Disp S
```

Solution (Continued)

2. Press $\boxed{Y=}$. Enter the expression to define Y1. Use

   $6 - 6X \wedge 5$

3. Press $\boxed{\text{RANGE}}$. Change the RANGE variable values.

   Xmin $= -1$ Ymin $= -10$ Xres $= 1$
   Xmax $= 2$ Ymax $= 10$
   Xscl $= 1$ Yscl $= 1$

4. From a blank line on the Home screen, press $\boxed{\text{PRGM}}$, select ⟨Prgm2⟩, and then press $\boxed{\text{ENTER}}$ to execute the program.

5. When the program executes, enter the lower limit (0), the upper limit (1), and the number of divisions (32) in response to the prompts.

   After calculating, the result is displayed.

   ```
   AREA=
           4.999999881
   ```

   Increasing the number of divisions increases the accuracy.

6. Display graphically the area calculated. From a blank line on the Home screen, press $\boxed{\text{2nd}}$ [DRAW] and select ⟨Shade(⟩. The completed expression is:

   Shade(0, Y1, 1, A, B)

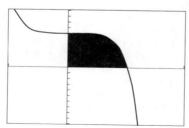

Program: Building a Table of Function Values

This program creates a table that maps a portion of a function's domain to its range.

Problem

Create a table of values for a function.

Specifically, create the table for X equal to -10, -9, ..., 9, 10 for the function

$$Y = 4 - X^2$$

Solution

The program calculates points on the function and stores them as statistical data points. It uses a 1×2 matrix to display each point as it is calculated.

1. Enter the program.

```
Prgm3 : FUNCTBL
:Disp  "XMIN"          Input Xmin
:Input  Xmin
:Disp  "XMAX"          Input Xmax
:Input  Xmax
:Disp  "N POINTS"      Input number of points
:Input  N
:DispGraph             Display the graph
:Pause
:Fix  2                Set mode
:ClrStat               Clear statistical data
:1→Arow                Define matrix for display
:2→Acol
:1→I                   Initialize:  Counter
:(Xmax−Xmin)/(N−                    Size of interval
1)→S
:Xmin→X                             Beginning point
:Lbl  1                Begin loop
:X→{x}(I)                Store values as stat data
:Y1→{y}(I)
:X→[A](1,1)              Store values in matrix
:Y1→[A](1,2)
:Disp  [A]
:Pause
:X+S→X                 Next point
:IS>(I,N)              Check for Xmax
:Goto  1               End loop
:
```

**Solution
(Continued)**

2. Press $\boxed{Y=}$. Enter the expression to define Y1. Use

   $4-X^2$

3. From a blank line on the Home screen, press $\boxed{PRGM}$, select ⟨Prgm3⟩, and then press $\boxed{ENTER}$ to execute the program.

4. When the program executes, enter Xmin (-10), Xmax (10), and number of points (21) in response to the prompts.

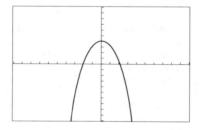

5. Press $\boxed{ENTER}$ after the graph is displayed.

6. Press $\boxed{ENTER}$ after each point is displayed.

7. After the program has executed, press $\boxed{2nd}$ [STAT] and select ⟨Edit⟩ from the STAT DATA menu to review the table.

Program: Plotting the Derivative

This program demonstrates the relationship between tangent lines at points along a function and the first derivative of a function.

Problem

Using the DRAW features of the TI–81, calculate and draw the tangent lines for a function and plot the slope (first derivative).

Specifically, using the default MODE settings, calculate and draw the tangent lines and slope for

$$Y = \sin X + 2$$

Solution

1. Enter the program.

```
Prgm4:TANGENT
:ClrDraw
:DispGraph              Display the graph
:Pause
:Disp "N POINTS"        Input number of points
:Input N
:(Xmax−Xmin)/N→S        Calculate size of interval
:Xmin+S/2→X             Define beginning point
:(Xmax−Xmin)/100        Calculate epsilon for NDeriv
→E
:Lbl 1                  Begin loop
:NDeriv(Y1,E)→M           Calculate slope
:PT−On(X,M)               Plot slope of tangent line
:Y1→Y                     Store value of function
:X−10E→A                  Define tangent end points
:Y−10EM→B
:X+10E→C
:Y+10EM→D
:Line(A,B,C,D)          Draw tangent line
:Pause
:X+S→X                  Next X
:If X<Xmax              Check for right of graph
:Goto 1                 End loop
:Disp "END"
```

**Solution
(Continued)**

2. Press $\boxed{Y=}$. Enter the expression to define Y1. Use

   sin X + 2

3. Press $\boxed{\text{RANGE}}$. Enter values for the RANGE variables appropriate for the function. Use

Xmin = -6	Ymin = -2	Xres = 1
Xmax = 6	Ymax = 4	
Xscl = 1	Yscl = 1	

4. From a blank line on the Home screen, press $\boxed{\text{PRGM}}$. Select ⟨Prgm4⟩ and then press $\boxed{\text{ENTER}}$ to execute the program.

5. A graph of the sine curve is plotted immediately. Press $\boxed{\text{ENTER}}$.

   When you are prompted, enter the number of points (20).

   The first tangent line and a point representing the slope are drawn on the graph. Press $\boxed{\text{ENTER}}$ to plot the next tangent and slope. Continue until the message **END** is displayed.

6. Press $\boxed{\text{GRAPH}}$ to view the resulting graph. The plotted slope points represent the first derivative of the plotted function, which for sin X + 2 is the function cos X.

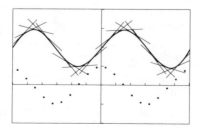

Program: Guess the Coefficients

This program graphs a function with random coefficients. You guess the coefficients.

Problem

Enter the program below, which assigns random integer coefficients between 1 and 10 to the function

a sin bx

The program displays the graph, and then you try to guess the coefficients.

Solution

1. Enter the program.

```
Prgm5 : GUESS
: Rad                      Set mode to Radians
: "AsinBX"→Y₁             Store target function
: IPart 10Rand+1→         Generate 1st coefficient
A
: IPart 10Rand+1→         Generate 2nd coefficient
B
: "CsinDX"→Y₂             Store your function
: 0→C
: 0→D
: −2π→Xmin                Set the RANGE variables
: 2π→Xmax
: −10→Ymin
: 10→Ymax
: π/2→Xscl
: DispGraph               Display the graph
```

2. From a blank line on the Home screen, press PRGM. Select ⟨Prgm5⟩ and then press ENTER to execute the program.

3. The graph is plotted immediately. (Since your function has coefficients of 0, it graphs "on" the axis.)

4. After you have figured out what you think the coefficients are, return to the Home screen.

5. Store your guesses in the variables C and D and press GRAPH.

6. Repeat step 5 until one function is graphed on top of the other.

Appendix A: Commands

This appendix lists the commands that are available on the TI-81.

Table of Commands

The commands on the TI-81 include functions, which return a single value and can be used in an expression, and instructions, which you enter on a blank line and which initiate an action. The F or I in the last column indicates if a command is a function or an instruction. Some, but not all, commands have arguments, which are defined here.

Commands and Arguments	Result	Menu/Keys	F/I Page
Absolute value: abs *arg1* •*arg1*: expression	Returns absolute value of *arg1*	2nd [ABS]	F 2-2
Addition: *arg1* + *arg2* •*arg1*: expression or matrix •*arg2*: expression or matrix	Returns *arg1* plus *arg2* Adds matrix elements	+	F 2-2 6-6
All-Off •no arguments	Unselects all functions in Y= list	2nd [Y-VARS] OFF ⟨All-Off⟩	I 3-19
All-On •no arguments	Selects all functions in Y= list	2nd [Y-VARS] ON ⟨All-On⟩	I 3-19
ClrDraw •no arguments	Deletes all drawn elements from a graph	2nd [DRAW] ⟨ClrDraw⟩	I 5-4
ClrHome •no arguments	Clears Home screen	PRGM EDIT PRGM I/O ⟨ClrHome⟩	I 8-13
ClrStat •no arguments	Clears current statistical data	2nd [STAT] DATA ⟨ClrStat⟩	I 7-3
Connected •no arguments	Sets mode to Connected line graph in a program	PRGM EDIT MODE GRAPH ⟨Connected⟩	I 8-16
cos *arg1* •*arg1*: expression	Returns cosine of *arg1*	COS	F 2-2
$\cos^{-1}$ *arg1* •*arg1*: $-1 \leq$ expression ≤ 1	Returns arccosine of *arg1*	2nd [COS⁻¹]	F 2-2
cosh *arg1* •*arg1*: expression	Returns hyperbolic cosine of *arg1*	MATH HYP ⟨cosh⟩	F 2-7
$\cosh^{-1}$ *arg1* •*arg1*: expression ≥ 1	Returns hyperbolic arccosine of *arg1*	MATH HYP ⟨cosh⁻¹⟩	F 2-7
Cube: $arg1^3$ •*arg1*: expression	Returns cube of *arg1*	MATH MATH ⟨³⟩	F 2-4
Cube root: $\sqrt[3]{arg1}$ •*arg1*: expression	Returns cube root of *arg1*	MATH MATH ⟨³√⟩	F 2-4

Commands and Arguments	Result	Menu/Keys	F/I Page
Deg •no arguments	Sets mode to Degree angle setting in a program	PRGM EDIT MODE NUMBER ⟨Deg⟩	I 8-16
Degree: arg1° •arg1: expression	Interprets arg1 as degrees	MATH MATH ⟨°⟩	F 2-4
detarg1 •arg1: matrix	Returns determinant of arg1 matrix	MATRX MATRIX ⟨det⟩	F 6-6
Disp "message" •message: text message, must include quotes	Displays text message, quotes not displayed	PRGM EDIT PRGM I/O ⟨Disp⟩	I 8-12
Disp variable •variable: variable, matrix, matrix element, stat data point	Displays value in variable	PRGM EDIT PRGM I/O ⟨Disp⟩	I 8-12
DispGraph •no arguments	Displays graph	PRGM EDIT PRGM I/O ⟨DispGraph⟩	I 8-13
DispHome •no arguments	Displays Home screen	PRGM EDIT PRGM I/O ⟨DispHome⟩	I 8-13
Division: arg1/arg2 •arg1: expression •arg2: expression ≠ 0	Returns arg1 divided by arg2	÷	F 2-2
Dot •no arguments	Sets mode to Dot graph display in a program	PRGM EDIT MODE GRAPH ⟨Dot⟩	I 8-16
DrawF function •function: function in terms of X	Draws function on graph	2nd [DRAW] ⟨DrawF⟩	I 5-7
DS<(variable,arg1) •variable: any variable valid for update •arg1: expression	Subtracts 1 from value in variable, compares to arg1, skips next command when variable < arg1	PRGM EDIT PRGM CTL ⟨DS<(⟩	I 8-11
e^arg1 •arg1: expression	Returns e raised to arg1 power	2nd [e^x]	F 2-2
End •no arguments	Ends program execution, returns to calling program	PRGM EDIT PRGM CTL ⟨End⟩	I 8-11
Eng •no arguments	Sets mode to Engineering display in a program	PRGM EDIT MODE NUMBER ⟨Eng⟩	I 8-16

Table of Commands (Continued)

Commands and Arguments	Result	Menu/Keys	F/I Page
Equal: *arg1* = *arg2* •*arg1*: expression •*arg2*: expression	Returns 1 if *arg1* = *arg2* Returns 0 if *arg1*≠*arg2*	[2nd] [TEST] ⟨ = ⟩	F 2–10
ExpReg •no arguments	Performs exponential model regression analysis	[2nd] [STAT] CALC ⟨ExpReg⟩	I 7–8
Factorial: *arg1*! •*arg1*: expression (0 ≤ integer ≤ 69)	Returns factorial of *arg1*	[MATH] MATH ⟨!⟩	F 2–4
Fix *arg1* •*arg1*: 0 ≤ integer ≤ 9	Sets mode to Fixed display with *arg1* decimal digits during program execution	[PRGM] EDIT [MODE] NUMBER ⟨Fix⟩	I 8–16
Float •no arguments	Sets mode to Floating display in a program	[PRGM] EDIT [MODE] NUMBER ⟨Float⟩	I 8–16
FPart *arg1* •*arg1*: expression	Returns fractional part of *arg1*	[MATH] NUM ⟨FPart⟩	F 2–6
Function •no arguments	Sets mode to Function during program execution	[PRGM] EDIT [MODE] GRAPH ⟨Function⟩	I 8–16
Goto *arg1* •*arg1*: label 0–9, A–Z, θ	Transfers program control to label *arg1*	[PRGM] EDIT [PRGM] CTL ⟨Goto⟩	I 8–10
Greater than: *arg1*>*arg2* •*arg1*: expression •*arg2*: expression	Returns 1 if *arg1*>*arg2* Returns 0 if *arg1* ≤ *arg2*	[2nd] [TEST] ⟨>⟩	F 2–10
Greater than or equal: *arg1* ≥ *arg2* •*arg1*: expression •*arg2*: expression	Returns 1 if *arg1* ≥ *arg2* Returns 0 if *arg1*< *arg2*	[2nd] [TEST] ⟨ ≥ ⟩	F 2–10
Grid Off •no arguments	Sets mode to Grid Off during program execution	[PRGM] EDIT [MODE] GRAPH ⟨Grid Off⟩	I 8–16
Grid On •no arguments	Sets mode to Grid On during program execution	[PRGM] EDIT [MODE] GRAPH ⟨Grid On⟩	I 8–16
Hist •no arguments	Draws a histogram of current stat data	[2nd] [STAT] DRAW ⟨Hist⟩	I 7–15

Commands and Arguments	Result	Menu/Keys	F/I Page
If *arg1* •*arg1*: expression	If *arg1* = 0 (false), skips next program command	PRGM EDIT PRGM CTL ⟨If⟩	I 8–10
Input •no arguments	Displays graph to explore with cursor during program execution	PRGM EDIT PRGM I/O ⟨Input⟩	I 8–13
Input *arg1* •*arg1*: any variable valid for update	Prompts for value to store to *arg1* variable during program execution	PRGM EDIT PRGM I/O ⟨Input⟩	I 8–13
Int *arg1* •*arg1*: expression	Returns greatest integer contained in *arg1*	MATH NUM ⟨Int⟩	F 2–6
Inverse: *arg1* $^{-1}$ •*arg1*: expression ≠ 0 or square matrix (det ≠ 0)	Divides 1 by *arg1* or inverts matrix	x⁻¹	F 2–2 6–6
IPart *arg1* •*arg1*: expression	Returns integer part of *arg1*	MATH NUM ⟨IPart⟩	F 2–6
IS>(*variable*,*arg1*) •*variable*: any variable valid for update •*arg1*: expression	Adds 1 to value in *variable*, compares to *arg1*, skips next command when *variable* > *arg1*	PRGM EDIT PRGM CTL ⟨IS⟩(>	I 8–11
Lbl *arg1* •*arg1*: label 0–9, A–Z, θ	Assigns label *arg1* to the program command	PRGM EDIT PRGM CTL ⟨Lbl⟩	I 8–10
Less than: *arg1*<*arg2* •*arg1*: expression •*arg2*: expression	Returns 1 if *arg1*<*arg2* Returns 0 if *arg1* ≥ *arg2*	2nd [TEST] ⟨<⟩	F 2–10
Less than or equal: *arg1* ≤ *arg2* •*arg1*: expression •*arg2*: expression	Returns 1 if *arg1* ≤ *arg2* Returns 0 if *arg1*>*arg2*	2nd [TEST] ⟨ ≤ ⟩	F 2–10
Line(*arg1*,*arg2*, *arg3*,*arg4*) •*arg1*: 1st x value •*arg2*: 1st y value •*arg3*: 2nd x value •*arg4*: 2nd y value	Draws a line from (*arg1*,*arg2*) to (*arg3*, *arg4*)	2nd [DRAW] ⟨Line(⟩	I 5–5

Table of Commands (Continued)

Commands and Arguments	Result	Menu/Keys	F/I Page
LinReg •no arguments	Performs linear model regression analysis	[2nd] [STAT] CALC ⟨LinReg⟩	I 7–8
ln *arg1* •*arg1*: expression > 0	Returns natural logarithm of *arg1*	[LN]	F 2–2
LnReg •no arguments	Performs logarithmic model regression analysis	[2nd] [STAT] CALC ⟨LnReg⟩	I 7–8
log *arg1* •*arg1*: expression > 0	Returns logarithm of *arg1*	[LOG]	F 2–2
Multiplication: *arg1* *arg2* •*arg1*: expression or matrix •*arg2*: expression or matrix	Returns *arg1* multiplied by *arg2* Multiplies matrix elements	[×]	F 2–2 6–6
arg1 nCr *arg2* •*arg1*: expression (integer ≥ 0) •*arg2*: expression (integer ≥ 0)	Returns number of combinations of *arg1* items taken *arg2* at a time	[MATH] PRB ⟨ nCr ⟩	F 2–8
NDeriv(*arg1*,*arg2*) •*arg1*: expression in terms of X •*arg2*: expression ≠ 0	Returns an approximate numerical derivative of *arg1* for delta of *arg2*	[MATH] MATH ⟨NDeriv(⟩	F 2–4
Negation: − *arg1* •*arg1*: expression or matrix	Returns negative of *arg1* Negates matrix elements	[(−)]	F 2–2 6–6
Norm •no arguments	Sets mode to Normal display in a program	[PRGM] EDIT [MODE] NUMBER ⟨Norm⟩	I 8–16
Not equal: *arg1*≠*arg2* •*arg1*: expression •*arg2*: expression	Returns 1 if *arg1*≠*arg2* Returns 0 if *arg1* = *arg2*	[2nd] [TEST] ⟨≠⟩	F 2–10
arg1 nPr *arg2* •*arg1*: expression (integer ≥ 0) •*arg2*: expression (integer ≥ 0)	Returns number of permutations of *arg1* items taken *arg2* at a time	[MATH] PRB ⟨ nPr ⟩	F 2–8
One-variable analysis: 1-Var •no arguments	Performs one-variable statistical analysis	[2nd] [STAT] CALC ⟨1-Var⟩	I 7–7
P►R(*arg1*,*arg2*) •*arg1*: r value •*arg2*: θ value	Converts (*arg1*,*arg2*) from polar to rectangular notation, stores in X and Y	[MATH] MATH ⟨P►R(⟩	F 2–4

Commands and Arguments	Result	Menu/Keys	F/I Page
Param •no arguments	Sets mode to Parametric graphing in a program	PRGM EDIT MODE GRAPH ⟨Param⟩	I 8–16
Pause •no arguments	Suspends program execution until ENTER is pressed	PRGM EDIT PRGM ⟨Pause⟩	I 8–11
Polar •no arguments	Sets mode to Polar coordinates in a program	PRGM EDIT MODE ⟨Polar⟩	I 8–16
Power of ten: 10^{arg1} •*arg1*: expression	Returns 10 raised to *arg1* power	2nd [10ˣ]	F 2–2
Powers: $arg1 \wedge arg2$ •*arg1*: expression •*arg2*: expression	Returns *arg1* raised to *arg2* power	∧	F 2–2
PT-Chg(*arg1*,*arg2*) •*arg1*: x value •*arg2*: y value	Changes point at (*arg1*,*arg2*)	2nd [DRAW] ⟨PT-Chg(⟩	I 5–6
PT-Off(*arg1*,*arg2*) •*arg1*: x value •*arg2*: y value	Erases point at (*arg1*,*arg2*)	2nd [DRAW] ⟨PT-Off(⟩	I 5–6
PT-On(*arg1*,*arg2*) •*arg1*: x value •*arg2*: y value	Draws point at (*arg1*,*arg2*)	2nd [DRAW] ⟨PT-On(⟩	I 5–6
PwrReg •no arguments	Performs power model regression analysis	2nd [STAT] CALC ⟨PwrReg⟩	I 7–8
R►P(*arg1*,*arg2*) •*arg1*: x value •*arg2*: y value	Converts (*arg1*,*arg2*) from rectangular to polar notation, stores in R and θ	MATH MATH ⟨R►P(⟩	F 2–4
Rad •no arguments	Sets mode to Radian angle setting in a program	PRGM EDIT MODE NUMBER ⟨Rad⟩	I 8–16
Radian: $arg1^r$ •*arg1*: expression	Interprets *arg1* as radians	MATH MATH ⟨ʳ⟩	F 2–4

Table of Commands (Continued)

Commands and Arguments	Result	Menu/Keys	F/I Page
Rand •no arguments	Returns a random number > 0 and < 1, seeded from value in Rand	$\boxed{\text{MATH}}$ PRB ⟨Rand⟩	F 2–8
Rect •no arguments	Sets mode to Rectangular coordinates in a program	$\boxed{\text{PRGM}}$ EDIT $\boxed{\text{MODE}}$ GRAPH ⟨Rect⟩	I 8–16
Root: $arg1 \wedge arg2^{-1}$ •$arg1$: expression •$arg2$: expression	Returns $arg2$ root of $arg1$	$\boxed{\wedge}$ $\boxed{x^{-1}}$	F 2–2
Round($arg1,arg2$) •$arg1$: expression or matrix •$arg2$: # of decimal places ($0 \leq$ integer ≤ 9) (optional)	Returns $arg1$ rounded to number of decimals in $arg2$ Rounds elements of matrix	$\boxed{\text{MATH}}$ NUM ⟨Round(⟩	F 2–6 6–6
RowSwap($matrix$, $row1,row2$) •$matrix$: matrix name •$row1$: expression •$row2$: expression	Swaps $row1$ of $matrix$ with $row2$, stores in result matrix	$\boxed{\text{MATRX}}$ MATRIX ⟨RowSwap(⟩	F 6–8
Row+($matrix,row1$, $row2$) •$matrix$: matrix name •$row1$: expression •$row2$: expression	Adds $row1$ of $matrix$ to $row2$, stores in $row2$ of result matrix	$\boxed{\text{MATRX}}$ MATRIX ⟨Row+(⟩	F 6–9
*Row($scalar,matrix$, row) •$scalar$: expression •$matrix$: matrix name •row: expression	Multiplies row of $matrix$ by $scalar$, stores in row of result matrix	$\boxed{\text{MATRX}}$ MATRIX ⟨*Row(⟩	F 6–9
*Row+($scalar$, $matrix,row1$, $row2$) •$scalar$: expression •$matrix$: matrix name •$row1$: expression •$row2$: expression	Multiplies $row1$ of $matrix$ by $scalar$, adds result to $row2$, stores in $row2$ of result matrix	$\boxed{\text{MATRX}}$ MATRIX ⟨*Row+(⟩	F 6–9
Scatter •no arguments	Draws a scatter plot of current stat data	$\boxed{\text{2nd}}$ [STAT] DRAW ⟨Scatter⟩	I 7–15
Sci •no arguments	Sets mode to Scientific display in a program	$\boxed{\text{PRGM}}$ EDIT $\boxed{\text{MODE}}$ NUMBER ⟨Sci⟩	I 8–16

Commands and Arguments	Result	Menu/Keys	F/I Page
Sequence •no arguments	Sets mode to Sequential plotting in a program	PRGM EDIT MODE GRAPH ⟨Sequence⟩	I 8–16
Shade(arg1,arg2, arg3,arg4,arg5) •arg1: function •arg2: function •arg3: expression (optional) •arg4: expression (optional) •arg5: expression (optional)	Shades area above arg1, below arg2, with resolution arg3, to right of arg4, to left of arg5	2nd [DRAW] ⟨Shade(⟩	I 5–8
Simul •no arguments	Sets mode to Simultaneous plotting in a program	PRGM EDIT MODE GRAPH ⟨Simul⟩	I 8–16
sin arg1 •arg1: expression	Returns sine of arg1	SIN	F 2–2
sin^{-1} arg1 •arg1: $-1 \le$ expression ≤ 1	Returns arcsine of arg1	2nd [SIN^{-1}]	F 2–2
sinh arg1 •arg1: expression	Returns hyperbolic sine of arg1	MATH HYP ⟨sinh⟩	F 2–7
sinh^{-1} arg1 •arg1: expression	Returns hyperbolic arcsine of arg1	MATH HYP ⟨sinh^{-1}⟩	F 2–7
Square root: $\sqrt{arg1}$ •arg1: expression ≥ 0	Returns square root of arg1	2nd [√]	F 2–2
Squaring: arg1^2 •arg1: expression or matrix	Returns arg1 multiplied by itself Squares matrix	x^2	F 2–2 6–6
Stop •no arguments	Ends program execution, returns to Home screen	PRGM EDIT PRGM CTL ⟨Stop⟩	I 8–11
Store a value: arg1→arg2 •arg1: expression •arg2: variable, matrix, matrix element, or stat data point	Stores value of arg1 into arg2 variable, matrix element(s), or stat data point	STO▶	I 1–20 6–10 7–16
Store expression to Y= list: "expression"→arg1 •expression: with quotes •arg1: function in Y= list	Stores expression to function arg1 in Y= list	STO▶	I 3–18

Table of Commands (Continued)

Commands and Arguments	Result	Menu/Keys	F/I Page
Subtraction: $arg1 - arg2$ •$arg1$: expression or matrix •$arg2$: expression or matrix	Returns $arg2$ subtracted from $arg1$ Subtracts matrix elements	☐	F 2-2 6-6
tan $arg1$ •$arg1$: expression	Returns tangent of $arg1$	TAN	F 2-2
tan^{-1} $arg1$ •$arg1$: expression	Returns arctangent of $arg1$	2nd [TAN^{-1}]	F 2-2
tanh $arg1$ •$arg1$: expression	Returns hyperbolic tangent of $arg1$	MATH HYP ⟨tanh⟩	F 2-7
tanh^{-1} $arg1$ •$arg1$: $-1 <$ expression < 1	Returns hyperbolic arctangent of $arg1$	MATH HYP ⟨tanh^{-1}⟩	F 2-7
Transposition: $arg1^{T}$ •$arg1$: matrix	Transposes elements of matrix	MATRX MATRIX ⟨^{T}⟩	F 6-6
xSort •no arguments	Sorts statistical data in order of X elements	2nd [STAT] DATA ⟨xSort⟩	I 7-6
xyLine •no arguments	Draws a line plot of current stat data	2nd [STAT] DRAW ⟨xyLine⟩	I 7-15
XnT-Off •no arguments	Unselects nth parametric equation pair in Y= list	2nd [Y-VARS] OFF ⟨XnT-Off⟩	I 3-19
XnT-On •no arguments	Selects nth parametric equation pair in Y= list	2nd [Y-VARS] ON ⟨XnT-On⟩	I 3-19
Yn-Off •no arguments	Unselects nth function in Y= list	2nd [Y-VARS] OFF ⟨Yn-Off⟩	I 3-19
Yn-On •no arguments	Selects nth function in Y= list	2nd [Y-VARS] ON ⟨Yn-On⟩	I 3-19
ySort •no arguments	Sorts statistical data in order of Y elements	2nd [STAT] DATA ⟨ySort⟩	I 7-6

Appendix B: Reference Information

This appendix provides supplemental information that may be helpful as you use your TI-81. It includes procedures that may help you correct problems with your calculator and it describes the service and warranty provided by Texas Instruments.

Updated Battery Information

The TI–81 uses two types of batteries: four AAA alkaline batteries, and a lithium battery as a back-up for retaining memory while you change the AAA batteries.

When to Replace the Batteries

As the batteries run down, the display begins to dim (especially during calculations), and you must adjust the contrast to a higher setting. If you find it necessary to set the contrast to a setting of 8 or 9, you will need to replace the batteries soon.

Effects of Replacing the Batteries

The effect of changing batteries is the same as turning the calculator off if you do not remove both types of batteries at the same time or allow them to run down completely. You should change the lithium battery every three or four years.

Replacing the Batteries

1. Turn the calculator off. Turn it over so that the back is facing you.

2. Holding the calculator upright, use your fingernail or a paper clip to push the latch on the battery cover down and pull the cover out.

3. Replace all four AAA alkaline batteries or the lithium battery. To avoid loss of information stored in memory, the calculator must be off; do not remove the AAA batteries and the lithium battery at the same time.

   - To replace the AAA alkaline batteries, remove all four discharged AAA batteries and install new ones as shown on the polarity diagram located in the battery compartment.

   - To replace the lithium battery, remove the screw and clip holding the lithium battery. Install the new battery, + side up. Then replace the screw and clip. Use a CR1616 or CR1620 (or equivalent) lithium battery.

   Dispose of used batteries properly. Do not incinerate or leave within reach of small children.

4. Replace the cover. When you turn the calculator on, the display shows the Home screen as it was when you last used it.

B–2   Reference Information

Accuracy Information

To maximize accuracy, the TI-81 carries more digits internally than it displays.

Computational Accuracy

Values in memory are saved using up to 13 digits with a two-digit exponent.

When a value is displayed, the displayed value is rounded as specified by the MODE setting (see pages 1-14 and 1-15), with a maximum of 10 digits and a two-digit exponent.

You can store a value in the RANGE variables Xmin, Xmax, Ymin, Ymax, Tmin, and Tmax using up to 10 digits.

Error Conditions

When the TI-81 detects an error, it displays an error message
ERROR *nn type* and a special error menu. The general
procedure for correcting errors is described on pages 1-26
and 1-27. The table below describes each error type in detail.

Error Codes

Code	Meaning/Suggestions
01 MATH	During evaluation, the absolute value of the result or an intermediate result was $\geq$ 1E 100. If the problem is an intermediate result, you may be able to reorder the expression or break it into two or more expressions.*
02 MATH	You are attempting to divide by zero.* You cannot calculate a linear regression that is a horizontal or vertical line.
03 MATH	You are attempting to calculate a root with an imaginary result.*
04 MATH	The command contains an invalid argument. See Appendix A and the appropriate pages of this manual. The result or an intermediate result is an imaginary number or is undefined.*
05 MATH	You are attempting to perform a matrix operation where the matrix is not appropriate to the operation. See page 6-7.
06 SYNTAX	The command contains a syntax error. Look for misplaced arguments or parentheses. See Appendix A.
07 MEMORY	An expression is limited to one intermediate matrix, 12 outstanding scalar operands, 30 outstanding parentheses, and two derivatives. You have exceeded one of these limits. You may be able to reorder the expression or break it into two or more expressions.

* Errors 1 through 4 do not occur during graphing. The TI-81
allows for undefined values on a graph.

Error Codes (Continued)

Code	Meaning/Suggestions
08 MEMORY	You are referencing a variable that is not currently defined. For example, you have not performed the statistical analysis that defines the variable you are referencing, or you are referencing a stat data point or a matrix element you have not entered.
09 MEMORY	There is no available memory in which to add additional statistical data. You must delete statistical data or delete or shorten a program.
10 MEMORY	There is no available memory in which to edit statistical data. You must delete or shorten a program. You cannot "go to" this error.
11 RANGE	• You have defined Xmax ≤ Xmin or Ymax ≤ Ymin. • The distance between Xmin and Xmax is too small to graph correctly. You cannot "go to" this error. Correct the RANGE variables. You can do this quickly by selecting ⟨Standard⟩ from the ZOOM menu to adjust the RANGE variables.
12 ZOOM	You are attempting to zoom in or out so far that the width of a dot is not within the numerical range of the calculator. You cannot "go to" this error.
13 BREAK	You have pressed the ON key to break execution of a program (see page 8-7), halt a DRAW instruction, or stop evaluation of an expression.
14 PRGM	The label in the Goto instruction is not defined with a Lbl instruction in the program.
15 PRGM	You are nesting program execution instructions (subroutines) more than 10 deep.

	Code	Meaning/Suggestions
Error Codes **(Continued)**	**16 INVALID**	You are referencing an invalid range.
		• **Xres** must be an integer between 1 and 8.
		• Matrix element dimensions must be positive integers between 1 and 6.
		• Statistical data point subscripts must be integers greater than zero.
		• **(Xmax −Xmin)/Xscl** must be ≤ 36 for a histogram.
	17 INVALID	You are referencing an invalid Y= function.
		• In function graphing, expressions to define functions in the Y= list cannot contain instructions, the **P►R** function, the **R►P** function, the variables Y or **Ans**, or parametric equations.
		• In parametric graphing, expressions to define parametric equations in the Y= list cannot contain instructions, the **P►R** function, the **R►P** function, the variables X, Y, or **Ans**, or Y= functions.
	18 INVALID	You are requesting a statistical analysis with fewer than two statistical data points. The frequency (Y value) for a **1-Var** analysis must be an integer ≥ 0.
	19 INVALID	You are referencing a Y= variable you have not defined.

In Case of Difficulty

If you have difficulty operating the calculator, the following suggestions may help you to correct the problem.

Handling a Difficulty

1. If an error occurs, follow the procedure on page 1-26. Refer to the more detailed explanations about specific errors beginning on page B-4, if necessary.

2. If you cannot see anything on the display, follow the instructions on page 1-5 to adjust the contrast.

3. If the keyboard is unresponsive, press ENTER. During program execution the **Pause** statement suspends program execution until you press ENTER.

4. If the calculator does not appear to be working at all, be sure the batteries are installed properly and that they are fresh.

5. If the difficulty persists, see page B-8 for information on contacting Consumer Relations to discuss the problem or obtain service.

Service Information

If the solutions suggested by "In Case of Difficulty" do not correct a problem you may have with your calculator, please call or write Consumer Relations to discuss the problem.

For Service and General Information

If you have questions about service or the general use of your calculator, please call Consumer Relations at:

1–806–747–1882

Please note that this is a toll number, and collect calls are not accepted.

You may also write to the following address:

Texas Instruments Incorporated
Consumer Relations
P.O. Box 53
Lubbock, Texas 79408

Please contact Consumer Relations:

• Before returning the calculator for service.

• For general information about using the calculator.

For Technical Information

If you have technical questions about calculator operation or programming applications, write to Consumer Relations at the address given above, or call 1–806–741–2663. Please note that this is a toll number, and collect calls are not accepted.

Express Service

Texas Instruments offers an express service option for fast return delivery. Please call Consumer Relations for information.

Returning Your Calculator for Service

A defective calculator will be either repaired or replaced with the same or comparable reconditioned model (at TI's option) when it is returned, postage prepaid, to a Texas Instruments Service Facility.

Texas Instruments cannot assume responsibility for loss or damage during incoming shipment. For your protection, carefully package the calculator for shipment and insure it with the carrier. Be sure to enclose the following items with your calculator:

- Your full return address and daytime phone number
- Any accessories related to the problem
- A note describing the problem you experienced
- A copy of your sales receipt or other proof of purchase to determine warranty status

Please ship the calculator postage prepaid; COD shipments cannot be accepted.

In-Warranty Service

For a calculator covered under the warranty period, no charge is made for service.

Out-of-Warranty Service

A flat-rate charge by model is made for out-of-warranty service. To obtain the service charge for a particular model, contact Consumer Relations **before** returning the product for service. (We cannot hold products in the Service Facility while providing charge information.)

Texas Instruments Service Facilities

U.S. Residents (U.S. Postal Service)
Texas Instruments
P.O. Box 2500
Lubbock, Texas 79408

U.S. Residents (other carriers)
Texas Instruments
2305 N. University
Lubbock, Texas 79408

Canadian Residents Only
Texas Instruments
41 Shelley Road
Richmond Hill, Ontario L4C 5G4

One-Year Limited Warranty

This Texas Instruments electronic calculator warranty extends to the original consumer purchaser of the product.

Warranty Duration

This calculator is warranted to the original consumer purchaser for a period of one (1) year from the original purchase date.

Warranty Coverage

This calculator is warranted against defective materials or workmanship. **This warranty is void if the product has been damaged by accident, unreasonable use, neglect, improper service, or other causes not arising out of defects in material or workmanship.**

Warranty Disclaimers

Any implied warranties arising out of this sale, including but not limited to the implied warranties of merchantability and fitness for a particular purpose, are limited in duration to the above one-year period. Texas Instruments shall not be liable for loss of use of the calculator or other incidental or consequential costs, expenses, or damages incurred by the consumer or any other user.

Some states do not allow the exclusion or limitations of implied warranties or consequential damages, so the above limitations or exclusions may not apply to you.

Legal Remedies

This warranty gives you specific legal rights, and you may also have other rights that vary from state to state.

Warranty Performance

During the above one-year warranty period, a defective TI calculator will either be repaired or replaced with a reconditioned comparable model (at TI's option) when the product is returned, postage prepaid, to a Texas Instruments Service Facility.

The repaired or replacement calculator will be in warranty for the remainder of the original warranty period or for six months, whichever is longer. Other than the postage requirement, no charge will be made for such repair or replacement.

Texas Instruments strongly recommends that you insure the product for value prior to mailing.

Index

This index contains an alphabetical listing of topics covered in this manual and their page references. (See also the Table of Commands in Appendix A.)